[Becoming]

Tues

~~Mon~~ 8/12   9-9³⁰ AM

"   "   11-11⁴⁵ PM

Wed 8/13   9-9⁴⁵³⁰ AM ||

              6³⁰-7¹⁰ PM

[Becoming]

Young ideas on gender, identity, and sexuality

Edited by Diane Anderson-Minshall
and Gina de Vries
Foreword by Zoe Trope

To order additional copies of this book, contact:
Xlibris Corporation
1-888-795-4274
www.Xlibris.com
Orders@Xlibris.com
24140

Contents

Section Three: [FAMILY, FRIENDS, CHOICES]

Section Four: [VIOLENCE, ABUSE, SURVIVAL]

Section Five: [LOVE, SEX, LOSS]

Section Six: [INTERVIEWS]

[Resources]

[ACKNOWLEDGEMENTS]

Like all anthologies, a lot of work went into this book—a great deal from people who don't get much credit. We could not have done it without a few people we must thank. First and foremost, thanks to Jessica Longo, our tireless editorial assistant who devoted many, many hours to the mind numbing research that produced our resource section. Jessica, a 23-year-old University of Chicago grad, just happened to be fighting a gallant battle against a quarter-life crisis at the time that we snagged her to work for us.

Another life crisis—this time a back injury—garnered us our copy editor. Susannah Anderson-Minshall spent many days flat on her back reading and rereading the manuscript and arguing with the editors about definitions of racism and where the damn commas should go in a sentence.

Our undying devotion goes to our cover photographer, Mea Tavares. His work was so amazing we couldn't believe we landed him for the cover. We owe him more than money can buy.

Thanks also to several contributors, notably Theresa Molter (who offered up an extensive list of suggestions for our reading list) and Grover (who did an excellent proofreading of our sometimes tedious glossary).

Feedback from several publishers and editors was helpful in shaping this work (notably from Karen Oosterhous at Firebrand Books and Leslie Miller at Seal Press) as were the comments from authors who reviewed us early on: T Cooper (the author of the great novel Some of the Parts), Lisa Jervis (publisher and editor of my favorite chick mag, *Bitch*), Lori Selke (the racy editrix of *Tough Girls*), and Rachel Kramer Bussel (the gal behind *The Lesbian Sex Book* and *Up All Night*). They all get our heart-felt thanks.

Oh, and the biggest, heartiest thanks goes to author Zoe Trope. Last year we fell in love with her brilliant memoir, *Please Don't Kill the Freshman*—the story of a her first year of high school in Portland, Oregon. Zoe's raw, jagged, smarmy juxtaposition of words jump off the page and the fact that she turned out such amazing work at 14 is all the more impressive. When she volunteered to write our foreword, both of us shrieked with joy. Thanks for making us shriek (it doesn't happen *that* often) and for introducing our equally jagged anthology.

[FOREWORD]

Kate Bornstein should be writing this, but she's busy applying lipstick and teaching workshops. Soon she'll be a professor, giving lectures at some elite university and her book, *Gender Outlaw*, will be required reading at every college from here to the moon.

Think I'm kidding? I'm not. Things change.

No, really, they do. 'Cause I used to have a girlfriend and she decided to be a boy and I used to be a dyke and now I like kissing boys until they get hard. You used to bite the heads off of animal cookies and now you sit in restaurants, making pleasant conversation until the bill arrives. You used to be one thing and now you're another. I bet, at one point, you used to be in love, and now you're not. Or maybe you weren't, and now you are.

What I'm trying to say is: This isn't permanent. This is so temporary.

Christo and Jeanne-Claude are environmental artists who romanticize the temporary. They take on elaborate projects involving buildings and rivers and trees wrapped in long stretches of lush fabric. Getting permission to shut down the Reichstag in Germany took years and years, but finally they were able to pursue their project. For two weeks, the building was transformed into an immobile ghost, a haunting figure draped in white. Thousands flocked to the display. It was mesmerizing, out-of-the-ordinary, and unexpected.

And it didn't last. It came down as quickly as it went up, and no evidence of the transformation remains, other than photographs, videos, and memories.

The preparation work for the project cost hundreds of thousands of dollars and the manual labor took weeks. It was so much effort expended for such a brief result.

But the result, however fleeting, was a sort of beauty that only happens once in a lifetime. I wish I could have been there to see it.

This isn't going to last. But at least I'm here to see it: Every stupid aching moment, every boy with sloppy eyeliner and every girl wrapping bandages around her breasts, every protest march and every flower bouquet, and every messy heart on every page of this book.

At least I'm here to see it.

With love,

Zoe Trope
March 2004

[DIANE'S INTRO]

It's hard not to notice queer people nowadays. It sounds simple, I know, but there are queer folks everywhere—on television and magazine covers, in rock bands and at high schools. My friends have gay doctors and lesbian realtors and transgendered ministers and bisexual bosses. It's no longer such a surprise to find out somebody is homo. Young people, it seems, are the least non-plussed by sexuality. Queer kids are suing their schools for not protecting them; they're declaring their orientation in elementary school; they're reinventing the dictionary to encompass the permeations of their life. I was not one of these kids. I was not very brave.

It was still the 1980s when I came out. There was a Bush in the White House but otherwise little was as it is now. Back then, 18 or 19 were considered young. Heck, I knew Mormon housewives who were coming out at 45. They thought *I* was revolutionary. In all honesty, I had a cadre of queer friends in my rural Idaho high school. Each weekend we drove sixty miles to the cool, all-ages, new wave dance where boys wore lipstick and girls danced with each other and we snickered at the drag queens and bar dykes who peopled the shadowy dive next door. None of us were out. My first boyfriend—the boy who gave me my first "real" kiss at 14—knew that he was gay long before that kiss (*I* knew that day). But we never talked about sexuality until we were in college. By that point, he'd had several boyfriends and I'd had a girlfriend for a year. A full closeted year where she and I double dated cute but clueless college boys who wondered why we spent so much time in the bathroom.

When I finally did come out, it shook my whole world. I moved dozens of times, transferred to six different colleges, and shifted all of my energies into queer activism. My parents were not pleased. I abandoned mainstream publishing for the burgeoning gay media. I found my home in feminist bookstores. Residing among other activists, I left work to attend ACT UP and Queer Nation protests and endlessly despaired about the plight of gay and lesbian youth locked away in mental hospitals by their parents. I wrote long diatribes about our lack of visibility at places like the 1987 March on Washington but I was too young, too disenfranchised myself to even make the trip. I was essentially still a teenager and—if you use the Stonewall Riots as the labor pains—so was the queer civil rights movement. There was no Ellen Degeneres or k.d. lang. Elton John and George Michael were still closeted. *Queer as Folk* and *Boys Don't Cry* were years away. Though Tim Curran came out as a gay Boy Scout in 1981, generally Scouts had not yet begun to declare their right to be gay. There were no lesbian rock stars, no gay television networks (no, MTV doesn't count). Plays about painfully shy gay teenagers—like Christopher Shinn's recent *FOUR*—did not attract mainstream reviews, much less straight audiences. There were no queercore indie bands like Bitch and Animal, Le Tigre, and Ninja Death Squad (whose song "Homophobes Gaybash in Order to Suppress Their Powerful Homosexual Tendencies" makes me smile every time). The AIDS Memorial Quilt—now so big it overflows the Mall in Washington—was small enough to fit in a car trunk. There was no Matthew Shepard.

Indeed, queer life in America has changed dramatically since I was young. Our civil rights movement—once focused on marriage and job security—now seems squarely in the hands of queer youth. A recent San Francisco State study shows that people are coming out at 14 and 15 instead of 19 and 20. Rather than dropping out of school and slinking away to some big city with this self-knowledge, this new generation is demanding to have a place in society, to be protected from harassment, and to have the same opportunities as its peers. When it doesn't happen—after all, a lot of queer kids still face a daily barrage of insults, threats, and assaults—some take matters into their own hands. They're not just forming gay-straight alliances and talking with reporters, they're also suing their schools: Derek Henkle, now 21, filed suit against his Reno, Nevada high school (seven years after he was beaten by fellow students) while19 year old Timothy Dahle just settled a federal civil rights case against his school district. Rosemary Linares launched a veritable campaign to get her Saline, Michigan high school to allow her to write about gay rights. Chris McCarthy and Mike Dillon put a halt to anti-gay harassment at their New Jersey school—and then formed a statewide group, Gay Youth Against Discrimination—to urge other teens to do the same. In Masconomet, Massachusetts, football captain Corey Johnson came out to his team, landed in *Sports Illustrated*, and raised queer youth awareness to a whole new level.

Nearly a quarter of a century after Randy Rohl and Aaron Fricke first did the same thing, a growing number of high school students are demanding to take their same sex dates to dances and proms. Just last year, couples in Toronto and Baton Rouge, Louisiana won the right to attend together. In Wyoming earlier this year, a straight senior (Amanda Blair) enlisted the help of the ACLU to challenge her high school's ban on same-sex prom dates. Sometimes, as in the case of Krystal Bennett, queer teens are defying gender while still being honored as prom royalty.

Of course, some of the change has happened at individual schools like Pennsylvania's Friends Central School—a Quaker school where classes now include "Gay and Lesbian Representation in Literature." Or like New York's Harvey Milk High School—the first and largest U.S. high school specifically for gay, lesbian, bisexual and transgender students—which is so popular that the dropout rate is minimal and there is a three-year waiting list. And in LA, Dr. Virginia Uribe's attempt to help gay students—Project 10, which was started just as I was coming out—has been so successful that the National Education Association has called for it's development nationwide.

Colleges, too, have seen a swell in queer activism, though this sometimes makes strange bedfellows: the all-woman Smith College has more out female to male trannies than any college of comparable size but rumor has it the administration will try to expel anyone who changes their legal gender or initiates physical transition. This keeps many transgendered Smith students in another type of closet but students are still showing their support: students just voted to change their constitution to gender-neutral pronouns to accurately reflect their increasingly trans population. Meanwhile, at Boston's Bridgewater State University, a new scholarship program became the first of it's kind; the Frank-Tremblay Safe Colleges Scholarship is aimed at gay and lesbian students who have been financially cut off by their parents.

This all underscores the real truth: that even though young queers have made remarkable advances, there is still peril in being yourself. A full 97 percent of students in public high schools hear homophobic remarks from peers. In fact, the typical high school student hears anti-gay slurs 25 times a day. At least 40 percent of homeless youth identify as lesbian or gay. Alcoholism, substance abuse, and depression are all significantly more common in LGBT youth. Queer teens account for 30 percent of all youth suicides (this includes, sadly, one of our contributors—Robbie Kirkland—whose mother submitted his poems). Though there are nearly one million gay teenagers in the U.S., parents and teachers are generally opposed to having any discussion of homosexuality in the classroom. Only 20 states require sex ed—most of it abstinence-based—and at least one in 12 health instructors teach their students that homosexuality is wrong. And, of course, queer kids are still having sex, sometimes with dire consequences. Lesbian girls have higher rates of teen pregnancy, and HIV infection among the young is still rising. For boys like Matthew Limon sex is fraught with perils. Matthew was sentenced to 17 years in a Kansas prison for having consensual oral sex with another teenage boy. Matthew had just turned 18 and his partner was a month shy of his 15th birthday but Kansas' "Romeo and Juliet Law" (a loophole for teen sex) doesn't apply to homosexuals. Matthew will be 35 when he gets out of prison and he'll have to register as a sex offender the rest of his life.

So, even though I envy the kids of today—their resources, their enthusiasm, their youth—you'll never catch me saying it's easy to be young and queer. Hell, it's downright perilous for transgendered kids. I can name off a handful of beautiful queer teens who were murdered in recent years: Gwen Araujo, Freddie Cortez, Alina Barragan, Ukea Davis, Stephanie Thomas. When 13-year-old Aaron Vays moved from Russia to New York so he could ice skate competitively, a group of gay-bashers put him in the hospital instead. After Andy Williams got tired of being taunted as a "wimp" and "bitch" at his high school, he went on a shooting spree that left two classmates dead.

But I do think queer youth today have one remarkable advantage over their predecessors—they get to live their adolescence in real time—and sometimes, occasionally, people listen to them. Mostly I think it's amazing to hear what young people today have to say. Hell, 16-year-old lesbian Emma Rood took on the government with a federal lawsuit against the Children's Internet Protection Act—which forces federally funded libraries to install filtering software that blocks controversial Web pages—because it prevented people from researching gay issues. Another 16-year-old, queer-identified Zoe Trope, became a cult hit with her novel *Please Don't Kill the Freshman*. Exploring geek love, lesbian debauchery, gay best friends, and general high school frustration, *Please* became a bestseller in Trope's native Northwest and garnered her a mainstream book deal from Harper Collins. The new memoir hits shelves before her 2004 graduation.

I love Zoe—I'm part of that so-called cult of fans she has now—and I think our vast array of our contributors should be getting the same accolades. Between interviews, essays, poems, plays, fiction, news reports, and song lyrics, my remarkable co-editor Gina deVries and I have assembled over three dozen great young minds. I couldn't be pressed to pick my favorite; they all lend themselves to the great diversity of ideas about gender, sexuality, and identity. (Heck, many of them couldn't even agree on the definitions of those words.)

Inside these pages you'll find Iolanta Star, a 16-year-old Russian immigrant teen, and Alicia Champion, a musician who self-produced her first album at 17. There's a lot of fierce poetry—on race and culture from the brilliant Sherisse Alvarez, on love and sex from Stanford's Ellen Freytag, and on just about everything from Holden Jude Dean, a 19-year-old genderqueer transboy. Montana-based Mikhail Lewis writes of a high school dance while James Patrick Gillece III talks, in even sparser prose, of finding love on the Internet. Matt Swanson, a 17-year-old from Wisconsin, gives us his thoughts on "real life" versus *Real World*. R.L. Baldwin boldly looks at race and family. Nadine Gartner presents a hilarious look at coming out to her Jewish mother. Christa Kreimendahl subverts the playwright genre (and gives me chills) with her award-winning play. Wendy Thompson, a 20-year-old bisexual, Chinese African American, and Shawnta Smith, a 19-year-old Jamaican/Belizean-Black American, both look at culture and identity as well as sexuality in their amazing pieces, while Grover—a trans-identified butch dyke leather boy drag king performance artist activist kid—offers up an essay on the racial politics of leather. Like many anthologies—especially ones in which the contributors range between junior high school students and college graduates—the work is intentionally uneven. Much of it is experimental and some of it reads like a visual effect from a spoken word piece. And it's challenging stuff to read—whether you're gay or straight. There are more pieces in this anthology than I can mention here. I think they each contribute a unique—and pressing—voice to *Becoming*. I hope you agree.

Diane Anderson-Minshall, March 2004 ♣

[GINA'S INTRO]

I came out as a lesbian when I was eleven years old. I sit to write this, many years and sexual permutations later, a month after my twentieth birthday. I'm in a late-night campus café at my small liberal arts college. My foot is moving back and forth to the hip-hop that the kids at the counter are playing. I can't hear much of what they're saying now—the music is too loud—but I heard the word "lesbian" a moment ago. Nobody flinched or made disgusted noises; nobody followed the word with a hateful expletive.

Most of the time, I can slip into that same mode of operation easily. I can say queer stuff and not worry that it will get a bad reaction; accept and understand the conversation that transpires as commonplace. In this world of mine, "I was talking with my genderqueer friend who wants to be a porn star" or "Have I told you about my intersex friend who was able to legally marry her partner?" sounds about as normal as "I had spaghetti for dinner."

Then I remember that in Catholic middle school eight years ago, even muttering the word "lesbian" in a vaguely positive way invited hurled epithets and basketballs that sent me running to the girls' room crying and clutching my broken glasses. I remember how scared I was when I was eleven and first acknowledging my crushes on other girls. I hid during recess at school and called youth hotlines at home, stammering into the phone at the disbelieving counselors on the other end: "Yes, I *am* gay. I *know* I'm only eleven, but that doesn't matter. I know who I am."

I began attending queer youth events and support groups at the Lavender Youth Recreation and Information Center in San Francisco, an organization that I credit with saving my life and my sanity as a scared middle-schooler. LYRIC gave me a sense of community and family, a refuge from the taunts and violence I faced at school. But still, in my first few months going there, the most common reactions to my age were "You're *how old?*" and "You're too young to even *have* a sexual orientation!" It was only after I stopped wearing dresses to LYRIC meetings and buzzed off my shoulder-length hair that people began to take me seriously. Now that I really *looked* like a little dyke, I must be genuine. When I was fourteen, I began examining and reclaiming my femme identity, and since I was older and had already "proven myself" to the queer community around me through activism and involvement, I was finally free to explore without people doubting my queerness.

I now visit LYRIC on my breaks home from college, to see old friends and staff and see how the youth there are doing. Now, there are tons of people in middle and early high school in attendance. In fact, the last time I visited there were probably more people in the 12 to 14 age range than there were college kids. I noticed that many of the younger dykes there were comfortable being feminine and being queer, that the two weren't mutually exclusive. I hope that if any of them have cut their hair since then, they've done it because they've wanted to, not just to fit in with the hip dyke crowd. The last time I visited LYRIC, I left feeling a mix of amazement and relief. I might have been the only 12-year-old there eight years ago, but that certainly wasn't the case now.

Sometimes, though, I forget how privileged I am to be in a place where I am safe; how privileged I am to talk about my queer, activist, pansexual, femme, sex-positive, pervert self and not really worry about the consequences. I remember what my life was like around this time eight years ago, and I am so thankful that I am no longer at my middle school, no longer having to explain and justify my right to be at queer groups just like the sixteen and seventeen-year-olds, no longer living the split reality of safety at LYRIC and terror at school. I am so thankful that younger people in the queer community are carving out a space for themselves that didn't exist when I came out.

How did I even get to a place where I have the luxury of forgetting? In leaving middle school, I was able to leave the harassment. The parochial school I attended through eighth grade was hardly accepting or supportive of my baby-dyke self, but when I got to high school, things were different. From ninth to twelfth grade, I went to a hippie school in the middle of San Francisco's Haight-Ashbury district. It was the kind of place where we sat in circles, called our teachers by their first names, and got narrative evaluations instead of grades. The kind of place that hung articles about my involvement with LYRIC on the bulletin board at the entrance to the school, with a circle around my name, a smiley face, and the annotation, "Gina is a Freshman Here!" Though I was the "Lesbian Poster Child" until I graduated (a fact that was particularly ironic to me considering my identity shift from lesbian to pansexual/queer) my high school was the kind of place where, even if kids didn't look past my sexuality they never viewed it as something bad or immoral. My teachers and friends in high school embraced and encouraged my queerness, gave me room to grow as an activist and writer, and, most importantly, treated me like a normal kid. I no longer felt that division between my school life and my outside life. Those spheres didn't need to exist separately any more, because I was finally safe.

Obviously, my high school experience was unusual. I went to a ridiculously expensive, small, private, alternative college-prep school, a school that I would not have been able to go to had I not been granted a partial scholarship (and had my parents not been able to foot the rest of the sizable bill). In large part, my parents' college education, my race, and my middle-class background privileged me to be in both a safe and an academically challenging and enriching high school environment. I know few people who have been able to take classes on

American labor organizing history, circus arts, and Russian literature by the time they graduate high school. I know even fewer queer people who have had the kind of high school experience that I have had, one where taunts and harassment were not part of their daily lives.

However, almost all of the young queer people I know, even if they never found support at school, found support in other ways: queer social and support groups, supportive spiritual communities, understanding family members, web pages, online journals and message boards, self-published 'zines, and both mainstream and underground-press books.

As a writer (and 'zinester and chapbook-maker), I have often wondered where support for queer youth—in all of our fabulous, diverse, and divergent identities—is available in the media. Where are the youth that came out young? Youth who realized they were queer but had more pressing issues at hand? Youth who have had multiple coming-outs and identity shifts? Where are trans and genderqueer and intersex youth, queer youth of color, queer working-class youth? With some notable exceptions (like Amy Sonnie's anthology *Revolutionary Voices*) the body of writing that is available to queer youth today is still painfully small, and it is lacking in both quality and diversity.

Too often, the voices that are heard within the queer community are still those who already hold privilege: white people, middle and upper class people, men, non-trans folks, people who identify as strictly "gay" or "lesbian" or "man" or "woman." Assimilation is a solution that many oppressed communities attempting to gain mainstream acceptance turn to—but at what cost? People of color, disabled people, bisexual, pansexual, transgender, transsexual, genderqueer, intersex people, BDSM-practicing folk, women, youth, and the elderly are most often ignored and silenced within the queer community. A large part of my personal writing and activism is figuring out ways to bring out the voices of these people and communities who are so often ignored and marginalized, and to acknowledge my own privilege as a white, middle-class, non-trans, "straight-looking," femme girl, and work to dismantle it. In the meantime, I try to use the privileges I have to open up avenues of communication, dialogue, and action for the communities and people I care about.

The voices represented in *Becoming* are an attempt to reflect the diversity and range of experience in the queer youth community. However, as much as Diane and I tried to find pieces that spoke to a wide range of experiences, there are still shortcomings. The number of MTF-identified trans contributors in this anthology is, to my mind, painfully small. There are, to my knowledge, no openly intersex contributors, nor are intersex issues discussed outright in any contribution. Representation of sex workers, deaf and disabled people, and working-class and poor people is scant. And while race, culture, and ethnicity are addressed in many of the pieces, I feel that the ratio of contributors of color to white contributors is still too low.

That is why, in part, I consider this a work-in-progress—not this anthology, per se, but the entire project of creating smart, diverse, and culturally-aware media for the queer youth community. My hope is that the places where this anthology is lacking will inspire our readers to carry on the work that Diane and I have begun. We hope others will want to further the body of diverse and radical media that is available to queer youth, and to make it with confidence and pride. I look forward to seeing how this anthology inspires and incites other queer youth to create their own media and give voice to their communities. I look forward to hearing from you, and, most importantly, seeing what you can do.

Gina de Vries, March 2004 ♣

Section One

[RACE, CULTURE, HISTORY]

TELLING CUENTOS,

TELLING STORIES

Sherisse Alvarez

Count your tellings. The girl's
got a pearl hanging off her necklace.
The trees be standing up to the train
in a reflection east by the descending sun.
I dyed
my hair pink
when I was 18 and couldn't help but think
I was becoming more white when really
I felt more connected to the colors that are
beautiful and allowed back home.
Not a home
I had visited but know through tradition
and ancestry. No, these are not lower-class colors there
not even on the flowers and ornaments at Naña's house.
No, there they are like a sanctuary
that make you want to kneel and pray and
be humble. Here in the institutions
you have to fight the split
fight believing
you are less without them

their white-only, English-only, male-only policies and systems,
    their
approval of your speech, your perspective, your attitude.
I am tongue-tied and split
by the color line by the anger by the black/white
cookie I paid $1.75 for. The sides
that I will never belong to but will always want to consume
by the price they put on our (other) blood
by the years Abuela worked for Liz Claiborne before they
sent her away with overworked hands
and $32 dollars a month to quiet them
by the misdiagnosed, drug-addicted mother missing
the reality of her own life because she's learned that she must
in order to survive.
By the hospitals that turn her
into a product, a productive citizen, a zombie,
a schizophrenic, a bi-polar, a manic-depressive
who only eats Hershey's bars and Cheese Doodles
and *dulces* Abuela will bring her from home,
by this here America, North America which we
often forget to say because we think that
America is the motherland and it ain't. We do not join
in the jungles of our sameness, in our queerness,
within our poetry, our desire to make the world
a better place.

Because part of my education
has been learning how to stand still long enough
to hear the insults, mostly quiet so we have to listen real hard,
like with a glass up to the wall. We do not come together
to form the circle where your ass is covered
and my hands are still the ones wiping down the mess.

When our grandmothers are the ones dressing your white children,
cleaning your white houses and hallways
and trying to speak your language while doing it.

When hormones are injected into the meat
of the slaughtered animal you will buy at your local supermarket
in order to make it more white.
You have no name for this.
We have no language
with which to articulate this
in your English. You will inevitably
correct it, say it does not sound proper,
say it does not sound sane.

I come corrected in an attempt to understand displacement.
We broken, been broke, continue to have no name
for the exiled. This is Taco Bell, the birth of humor
to replace namelessness. An advertisement
for the Mashantucket Pequot Museum.
Indians, Indigenous Peoples, Native Americans.
Rooms and glass cases filled with artifacts and abolished his/her
    stories.
Magnificent. It brings the national Native American story vividly
    to life.
What story is that. I've stopped believing all their stories.
The work that comes,
where to begin it. ♣

EVEN WHEN LEAVING

THE GHETTO

Shawnta Smith

If the reader of this essay knows nothing of Borough Park, Brooklyn which is a ghetto inhabited with Orthodox Jews, then the experience of an interracial lesbian couple in residence here must be explained as comfortable only for the newcomers, and not its locals. We've lived here less than two months and already my girlfriend and I suffer an intolerable silence from our fellow neighbors. I see it as a journey; they see it as an invasion. However, regardless of the repressed homophobia, alive and forthright, their vow of silence, keeps us happy.

At the LGBT Alliance in Brooklyn College where I attend, a lesbian Jewish member points out that walking in Borough Park for her is a voyage just because she wears pants as a female, and on a basis of respect, she would never walk hand-in-hand with her girlfriend there. Sadly, I disagreed with her. For the obvious reasons of me being a Black woman with locked hair, and my girlfriend being a Latina woman with a boyish exterior, we lack the luxury of "passing" as straight Jewish girls, and politically, choose not to disguise our identities.

On Friday nights, there is the ceremonial Sabbath that ends on Saturday night. On these nights, the town remains quiet. No one speaks to anyone unlike herself, or even to her own mind (this still remains a mystery to me). All stores are closed; all cars have come to a halt. My girlfriend and I love these nights deeply, possibly because during Sabbath, we are alone, we own the streets, for no one is outside to scorn our existence, even if only once a week. There is a serene peace that overtakes us on a night when our usual reality would be to go clubbing. We appreciate the silence of our loud lives in a neighborhood where we are seen as outcasts. There, we find our peace.

Most times we walk past Eleventh Avenue to the park where the hockey court lies. It is amusing to us that there is a hockey court here; during our childhoods there were only basketball courts with broken hoops. Aside from the occasional Mexican flower vendor, there are no black or brown faces; we learn that those who choose to speak to us are the Polish laundromat and the Italian pizza shop owners. We joke around that we can sit in the park for only an hour, before someone calls the police.

Going to school is the only time that I am here without her. I wait for the B11 bus to pass my way straight to Brooklyn College on Bedford Avenue. These times, I watch the loud streets as silent as I am watched on Sabbath. There is a separate bus and van line that I am understandably forbidden to ride. I am unsure if it requires special membership or genetic manipulation, but my experience has been waiting in the cold, while Jewish passengers get a seat. Because I am alone, I presume, a Jewish woman invites me to take the van with her. I wonder if it is because I wear a long black woolen coat like she does, or because she is also as anxious as I am standing alongside a "different" woman. Of course I do not get on, we discover that we are going different ways, almost an intentional discovery. Nevertheless, the invitation surprised me, and I began to question whether or not the subversions were all in my head.

Lately, I have been a lot more comfortable, and have become accustomed to the stares of pretense by my neighbors. I will assume that everywhere, in every community of the nation, these stares will be the same, so expecting different from one group would be expecting different from society. As a black lesbian in an interracial couple, I will relish in the beauty and culture of Borough Park as a part of my journey. But I refuse to apologize for my way of living, as I do not expect the orthodox Jews to do so for me. I'm hoping for comfortable living in the future. A neighborhood where respect, dignity, and true happiness can be found, not only on Sabbath night, but always. ?

SCARED

Wendy M. Thompson

does it matter.
between the lips.
the neck.
the fingers.

does it hurt.
my eyes, my mind.
this intent.
this thing inside me that makes you afraid.
does it kill you to know I'm not like the other girls
I'm not like the boys.
that I would give all for you.
die for you.
and love you like no other.
and after I'm done explaining it, you will see that my skin is
     brown.
you will only know what you know: that this daughter.
this small woman born to oppressed people
born to colored people
born to straight people
was capable of loving you. ♣

THE FIRST

(CULTURE FUCK)

Wendy M. Thompson

I saw her for the first time
Standing in front of a dressing room mirror
Trying on a bathing suit that fit too loose over too small limbs
Her slant eyes bitter
Her mouth twisted down
It was no accident
The disoriented oriental outgrowing her place
Like a wild untamable stalk of sugar cane
Japanese Godzilla made in the USA
Towering over buildings water towers
Overturning vehicles and corrupting freeways.
For the first time I was seeing me
It was a distorted reflection
The half black Asian girl
The only person darker than the super smart fob kids in my
    English honors class
Stuck at home on Friday nights
Only to turn 18 one day and leave home with plans for the prom
My mother standing in the doorway
My father behind her
His fists balled up

Her mouth the shape of an O
A maddening scream in Mandarin
About how dare I walk out the house wearing that
that they ache knowing that I am unstoppable
a little brown girl born out of broken English
stuffing herself with bao and rice while her immigrant mommy
    tells her be a good girl
be polite study hard and smile
yet I was not good enough
I was not polite
And I didn't study hard.
My aunts wanted me to be pretty
They fed me lies at my po po's house about how
If I ate all the bok choi on my plate
I would one day be Miss Chinatown
With a diamond tiara stranded in my curly black hair
The sash covering a chest where breasts should be
I was never as good looking as I should have been.
But I was the number one daughter
No sons
Just three girls
Bad luck
And arguing
Mama crumpling to the floor after daddy hits her in the head
    with the door of the freezer
I hated that refrigerator ever since
Black daddy yelling at yellow mommy about not understanding
    English
Stupid motherfucker, he says
I act like I don't hear it.
I don't hear a lot of things
The way my father is disappointed for not having a son
And in my act to appease him
He calls me stupid
Confused
He says I am needing therapy

Because I act like a man (dysfunctional)
All macho
Pretending
I do not know how to cry
I talk loud and mask my body with XXL clothes
I make myself look bigger than I am
act like the tough guy and challenge boyfriends to fights
Coming home with a smashed nose
Bloody black eyes
I do not report it when they rape me
The first and the next
Proving that they are real men
Realer than my fake acts of survival
They get offended when I say I like girls
They feel threatened
And establish the boundaries by saying that I will never have a
    dick to please her with
My sesame seed girl on top of my brown rice body
They say she won't fall for it
Bullshit
But still we act it out
Like gender fucked Barbie dolls
Me being the man-woman
And her
This girl with the Sanrio fetish who likes to buy Tapioca drinks in
    Chinatown
Her round moon face
Her body twisting like a root inside and outside of mine
Bending out of tradition
She is not straight but won't admit she's gay either
Her sex split in halves like her culture
1.5 korean american/female sexed with thoughts laced with me.
Undercover from her immigrant mother who can't quite roll the r's.
And I remember it like the first day we met
Or the first day I looked at her and we kissed
She wasn't like the other girls,

She didn't pull away
I remember how we faked it
Told her mom we were going upstairs to try on a new dress
When her mother suddenly burst into her bedroom and found me
doing that to her daughter spread-eagled and naked from the
    waist down
that it was no longer funny
the language had ceased
our little fling ended with the shunning of my disloyal identity
I had ruined that chance to prove my Asian-ness
To disown the part of me that was rotten
The apple that Buddha never blessed
Turning mute the eyes growing accustomed to the dark
her two eyes never seeing that way again and after her
    disappearance they all became white
like white walls and white sheets
white lovers like buttered popcorn and candy apple
numbing my tongue
scarring my taste
no more fish balls snapped up in cross legged chopsticks
rubbing together like lovers the dim sum
passed for a meal of fast food burgers and fries.
I walk this world alone seeing signs in Spanish
that hang in the greasy windows of Little Asia
now serving American cuisine
curtains browned and shut like her legs and her mind.
a whispered reminder of how English was never spoken here ♣

ASIANASIAM

Han Yu

Asian as I am,
I live in a land
Unclaimed of Chinese origin.
Though I was born There
I am not of the world here;
not quite an American citizen,
though I hold the proper passports
of paper and manner.
Asian as I am,
my mother knows the handicaps of a Chinese face
better than myself.
there was the time
when I despised her inept American attempts,
misunderstanding.
O god what a stark shame
that she and dad are foreign
in a place that I'd rather not be.
Asian as I am,
I enunciate clear clipped English
in declamatory tones.
I am educated all American
and in love with exotic white women.
I do two kinds of belonging,
anonymity and leadership,

with the grace of native knowing.
Chinese
Japanese
my knees
look at me
I am decorating myself with ways of being
that I am born capable of,
but am not.
as easily American as I am Chinese,
sprouted in Asia and rooted U.S.A. O.K.
time has come for me to extend through
seas
to peoples and continents
connected yet unseen
and new parts of me. ♣

WHEN LEATHER IS NOT

JUST BLACK AND WHITE

Grover Wehman

In everyday life in New York City, my style of dress, gender expression, and the company I keep usually declare my politics as soon as I walk in a room. Part of my draw to the leather lifestyle is the opportunity for me to escape from the constant chatter in my head. Deconstructing the racist/sexist/capitalist implications of every advertisement and government presence on the street sends me into a healthy youthful rage, fueling the activism and work that is central to my life. When my life is my activist action, it is just as important for me to let loose and simply focus on being sex positive and feeling good. As an anti-racist, white, leather kid submissive, how do I maintain safe space and confront issues of racism when they arise after I have turned in my silk-screened "fuck yer racist war" patched hoodie for the white button down oxford cloth?

Attitudes and politics are as diverse as their beholder in HankieLand as everywhere else. I am sure I'm not alone in experiencing times when the company I am serving has made a racist (or sexist, homophobic, fat-phobic, or anti-trans) remark. Often it is in passing and usually I feel I must let it slide in err to my submission. There are times, however, when one slightly offensive comment turns into more racist comments and I find myself in an unsafe situation. I feel as if being white feeds into this situation because there is a feeling of safety "amongst family" in the oppression of others. This has become seemingly truer in lieu of our present war, mainstream's interpretation of race as black and white, and mainstream society's acceptance of the dehumanization of Arab and Muslim following September 11th. While I work to value all opinions, I am aware when I am in an unsafe situation and when the line has been crossed between stating an opinion and simply being racist. I have been fortunate in serving anti-racist Tops whose politics are pretty much in line with my own. However, what about the times when I may feel unsafe and my Top has not disputed the comments in a way that makes me feel secure and made safe the environment to a state that I find acceptable? What does one do when a bottom/sub failed to put "no racist remarks" on hir yes/no/maybe list? As an anti-racist person who is insulted and feels unsafe around racist, hate-seeped remarks, I am in quite a bind (sometimes literally).

With all honor and respect for my space of submission, I feel as if this is a situation in which I must state my feelings of not being safe. Sometimes, if one is lucky enough to have a Top who knows hir well enough, all it takes is a change in hir body language for the Top to get the message loud and clear that ze is feeling unsafe and uncomfortable by the racist rhetoric enveloping hir. Hopefully your Top will advocate for you or come to realize independently why what is being said is not okay and make a statement against it. In the event that your sudden stop of the shoeshine rag or tightening of back muscles are not effective, I feel it is imperative in all safe/sane/consensual logic to discreetly whisper to your top "I am feeling unsafe by these racist remarks." If that doesn't work, then you would have the right to either ask permission to leave the room and excuse yourself, making a silent statement. Or by all means, if you are feeling unsafe enough and feel as if your top is not respecting your sense of safety by putting an end to the comments, this might be a good sign that you may want to consider using your safeword. Ideally, thinking about your mental and emotional limits would be something that would be good to consider when doing pre-negotiations and developing a yes/no/maybe list.

Sadly, this world is far from ideal, yet it seems unnecessary to have to bring your slingshot day planner to a scene or develop a special hankie to announce your anti-racist radical leanings. Racism is always uncalled for and unexpected, especially when one is entering a space with the expectation of being happy and safe. Someone saying something you disagree with in your presence is one thing, someone making an unsafe and hostile environment, especially when one is in such a vulnerable position as sub space, is another. Safety is not always about the equipment and how long ago your bruises went away. The effects of racist remarks attacking your dignity and soul will leave a much deeper scar than any single tail or rope burn ever could. ♣

STONEWALL

tyger walsh

dedications
for the trans-men and women who defended their livesin the
    Stonewall Rebellion in NYC 1969
and the Compton's CafeteriaRebellion in San Francisco1968.for
    the lovely and fabulicious members of
TransAction.for freedom fighters everywhere.

Absence
what you search to fill
with every pill popped
praying not to feel
tearing of rocks and razors
gutting dreams from the bottom
of your belly where the visionary
the prophet
the healer
the hope, the creator in you used to live
now where the thunder of hideousness rumbles
persistent like beatings
from police, employers, strangers, family
convincing you
to be the monster we see on TV
Ricki Lake Sally Jesse Jerry Springer
you know the fucked up contortions

they force your reality into
justifying this grotesque punishment
this is for the queens
    the fairies
    the high maintenance femmes
    the stone butches
    the 24/7 transsexuals
    the gender benders
I pay homage to my predecessors
It is becuz of you
that I can flaunt my desire
for lipstick and silicone dicks lips sticking to
clits
this shit is not sick
you taught me to carry pride
in my panties proud of heavy pantings
the way our queer hearts love is nothing less
than spiritual perfection endless complications
of beautiful never settle for less
than freedom
your herstory is built on stone walls
you beat back the prison cells of gender with
martini glasses bar stools and
high heels
using your beauty as a weapon
you stopped billy clubs and pistols
with bar stools and
high heels

now 32 years later
I benefit from your struggle
we all do
queer youth coming out younger
and younger expanding the boundaries of gender
normalities further and further but the struggle
continues cuz the billy clubs don't stop

searching for mini skirts with dicks
gender police pricks still criminalizing your
identity
our families still unforgiving
not realizing they got blessed

so I kneel and pray that you reclaim the sunshine
in your smile the tree trunk curve
of your spine you are divine
and always have been indigenous women humbly
approach you asking for a blessing cuz they know
you are closer to god
occupying the promise land between male and female
your resistance the roots of rebellion
unearthing the atrocious truth of this capitalist
system
so breathe full bellied
dreams of liberation
melt the rocks and razors
make room for the goddess in you to lead us
forward in this fight towards freedom
towards justice towards life
open lungs expand hearts
breathe us towards life
in this fight for our lives. ♣

Section Two

[IDENTITY, IMAGE, SELF]

I CALL MY GIRL A BOY

SOMETIMES

Theresa E. Molter

I call my girl a boy and she gets mad. Defensive. She yells, "I'm not a boy!" and tackles me to the ground, pinning my arms behind my head and kissing me hard on the mouth to prove to me just how much of a girl she is. She tells me she's not a boy—maybe it's mean of me to say this to her. She wants to be a girl.

She has strict definitions for herself of what a girl is, despite having chronic crushes on all the tranny boys in Portland. Maybe she gets so mad because she's not always feminine.

She compares herself to me, I think. I have hips—she doesn't. I paint my nails and buy expensive cosmetics. She doesn't see the point, and while it makes me feel self—confident and glamorous, for her it becomes an act—something she only does on a special occasion. She plays dress-up. But it's not her. (She doesn't feel natural) I had my hair cut short when I was trying to be a good dyke. I looked like a pixie, my wisps of curly hair hanging in my eyes. When I tried to spike it up it just looked silly. My girl cut her hair short and messed it around with pomade and looked like the hottest, toughest dyke in town in her bright red "American Auto Wrecking" shirt. She tried to look like a girl with her short hair, wearing little bobby pins and headbands. But she hated it. She told me she felt like one of those babies whose mother puts a stretchy headband around her hairless head and dresses her in pink in order to distinguish her from a boy. She stopped trying.

My girl is tougher than me. I play tough in wife beaters and sports bras, flexing what little muscle I have. I growl but act cute. I break out in laughter when I'm trying to look serious. I put my weight onto one leg, my hip jutting out. She tells me that's not the way to stand if I want to be tough. She doesn't try to act tough. She's sullen, forgetting that she's given up the goth look. When I tempt her into giggling, she still gets mad at me sometimes.

She never cries. I cry weekly—it helps me to deal with stress and emotions. I am the stereotypical girl this way. I am not a wall of steel. She has seen me cry, has held me around the waist as I curl into a ball with knees against my chest and sob. She has watched me as I cry over fights with parents, over friends whose lives I hate to see fucked up, over her. My girl can count on one hand the number of times she has cried in the past ten years. I have seen her cry twice in the three years I have known her, and remember each instance. When we saw *Boys Don't Cry* she got teary-eyed. When she was frustrated with a professor. She told me she cried when she crashed her mother's car. She does not cry when she is hurt, physically or emotionally. She sucks it up. Takes it like a man, you might say.

My girl is self-sufficient. She does not like to feel helpless, girly, useless. She likes to be equal to boys on their own turf. She likes to learn useful skills in order to become more independent. Together we have taken carpentry, we have changed the oil on a car, we have welded metal. I wouldn't have done any of this without her. I don't know how to jump-start a car. I can barely pop the hood. I don't even know how to recline the seat sometimes. I can't drive stick shift. I'm an awful driver. The idea of carpentry, metalworking, power tools intimidates me. When men try to teach me these things, they don't look me in the eyes. They don't ask me to try it myself. They do it for me. Because of this, I let them. Because of this, she wants to beat boys at their own games. I like the outer image of being tough, but I usually feel that there are people better suited to building my furniture, fixing my car, carrying heavy boxes, than I am. Maybe because my mom didn't know how to do these things, she didn't tell me I should learn how to do them. Maybe because even my dad didn't know how to do these things. (I think he's a femme too.)

My girl makes boys show her how to do things, instead of watching. When someone says, "I need two strong boys to lift this table," she always gets up and does it in protest. Not because she feels like a boy, but to combat sexism. (But I'm a feminist too.) My girl's mom taught her she could do whatever she wanted, just like my mother did. But we want to do different things. I write because my mother encouraged it. She never bothered to tell me that it's not a successful career, instead telling me to follow my dreams. My girl's mother told her, "Don't be a wimp." Her mother used to read her a book about a girl who wore overalls and wanted to build a box. My girl's teacher told her only boys build boxes and girls play house. She cried to her mom and dad and they told the teacher that she could build a box and play house. So she fixes things and builds shelves for the bathroom, and I stand around breathing in the sawdust, handing her tools and asking questions, trying not to get too dirty.

She bakes cookies, too. My girl's mother taught her how to cook and pushed her to be tough. She is a master in the kitchen. She cracks eggs and separates yolks from whites without breaking them. She knows the different spices to use for making Indian curries and Italian pasta sauces. She bakes bread that comes out perfectly crusty on the outside, soft and moist on the inside. My friends request her to bake their birthday cakes. We have cooking parties and craft parties. We have been dubbed the Queer Martha Stewarts by our friends. My girl knits as much as someone's grandma. She tries to teach me but I am impatient, fidgety, can't get it right as hard as I try. I prefer to stick to cutting and pasting, inhaling rubber cement fumes. I can't figure out which one of us is the housewife. She plants flowers and weeds the garden, cultivates vegetables, picks tomatoes and has fresh salsa waiting for me. I go out with my friends, have drinks, come home to her reading on the couch. (It all equals out somehow.)

We both look like girls in gauzy dresses and mary janes when we go out at night, holding hands while walking down the street. Older dykes smile and wink. Drunken frat boys stop us on the street. "Is that your sister? Can I get your sister's number?" We both look like girls and we both act like girls, and sometimes we act like boys. We do what we want. I tell her she's the butch, I tell her she's a boy and she gets frustrated and points out all the things I do (or don't do). We have come to an unspoken agreement to stop trying to define ourselves. If we were a heterosexual couple, I think she'd be the housewife, because she cooks and gardens and wants to be a mother. But in our relationship now, I pin her as the butch, because she doesn't cry and likes power tools. Maybe she's neither. And if she's both, what does that make me? ♣

LIFE AS AN EX-GAY

POSTER CHILD

Wade Richards

When I was 12 years old, I started going to a Pentecostal church. I was heavily into my church youth group and led a junior Bible club on campus. When I was 15, after a good, solid year of fasting and praying, and having the church pray that God would change me and make my homosexuality leave, I was just discouraged. I said, "You know what? This is a big joke. I'm gay and can't change my sexual orientation."

When I was 15, I signed myself out of high school. It was the first week of my sophomore year in high school. I have no idea why I was allowed to do that. I was a rambunctious high school student, so maybe they were relieved when I left. So, I signed myself out and ran away from home.

At that time, I didn't have any adult supervision, no role models, no gay peers, and I just went down a road of destruction. All I knew were gay bars. That was all that catered to the gay community back then, except for MTV's *Real World* and *Ricki Lake*—there was just those tidbits of gays on television. I had nothing, really. So, I got into drugs and having all sorts of awful relationships, not knowing who I was at all. That went on for about three years, until I was 18. I had not been home since I was 15 years old.

I was afraid of sex, because the whole AIDS thing was going on and really in your face. MTV did an incredible job of getting the information out there while I was growing up, like with the whole Pedro Zamora thing, and I followed *The Real World* very closely. That whole thing with Pedro was going on when I was 15, so at least in all my chaotic mess and unhealthy behavior, it scared me enough to not be as promiscuous as I could have been. I was just looking for intimacy; as long as I was physical with someone in any way, there was intimacy.

I had no passion for life. I had no goals, no direction, and no one to tell me. All I knew about the gay "lifestyle" was what I saw on *Ricki Lake*. Honestly. I just thought it was all about partying and going to gay bars, because I had been getting into gay bars since I was 15-years-old. I was fresh meat, and I got invited to all these parties and to nude beaches.

My mom and dad divorced before I was even a year old. All my life, I was really starving for male affirmation and male attention and male affection. I found that by going to gay bars—although it was inappropriate, it was there, and it was real.

When I was 18, I moved to New York City to work as a houseboy for a gay couple, but the job fell through. I realized I was making some major life-altering choices and I needed to take inventory of my life. Instead of moving back to Wisconsin, where I was from, I decided I was going to stay in New York, with forty dollars, live at Covenant House Youth Shelter, and pick up my life from the pieces I had left at that point.

Some of the girls that lived in the youth shelter had invited me to go to Times Square Church in New York City. It's a huge 5,000-member church, and the pastor had ties to the church I had started going to when I was 12. So, there were ties there, and it was neat to be in New York City and see this pastor I met when I was 12-years-old at this youth conference, who actually prayed for me when I was that age.

I was in this 5,000-member church, and the pastor pointed to me and said, "God has a plan for your life, Wade." There were a group of men at the church who just took me in and loved me, and weren't afraid of my effeminate behavior. They loved me where I was at, for no charge. I didn't have to have sex with them. They didn't want anything from me. It really changed my life. They were everything I didn't think a heterosexual man was. Every heterosexual man I had known had beaten me up, called me faggot, or wanted to use me for sex. I started doing Bible studies with them, and they just said, "God's desire, Wade, is for you not to be gay." I was like, "Goodness gracious, I've been down this whole road before. I can't imagine going through the anguish and trying to change this again. But if God brought me this far, you know, and all these things have happened, maybe I am not gay."

My life was a perfect picture of what the Christian Coalition and Exodus International say the lifestyle is. It was a perfect example of someone who would be ex-gay. Their teachings taught that I wasn't really homosexual, I was just vulnerable to homosexuality. That was the means to receive male affirmation, male affection, and male attention—three things I craved. My pastor mentioned to me that he had mentored someone out of homosexuality, who was the executive director of Love In Action International, and they had just moved from California to Tennessee. So, I contacted them, and they said, "You're really young. We've never had someone your age go through the program and succeed." In my interview process, I told them that this was life or death for me. I'm not playing. I was on the streets, literally. I needed this program like I needed the air I'm breathing now. They accepted me, and my life changed overnight. I went back to school and got a diploma—all these positive life altering things happened. I started changing my character.

I began to be applauded for all these small steps. They all thought, this must really work. How amazing that because of Love In Action I was changing my sexual orientation through the power of God and the steps in this program. But what was really changing was my character and behavior traits. The psychological steps that they use, which are also part of the twelve step programs, they *do* work. Narcotics and Alcoholic Anonymous work. When you are serious about it, you can change your traits, your behavior. But I thought I was literally having my sexual orientation changed.

I graduated from the program successfully, was accepted to Bible college, and thought I would have this picture-perfect life now. I started dating a girl who was one of my very good friends in New York City. She moved down to Memphis to go to Bible college with me, then I got accepted to work with this national Christian youth organization in Los Angeles. Love In Action is a residential ministry. You live there. It's not just something you go to bi-weekly. They are very sheltered and strict and you're under 24-hour surveillance. So, I left my very sheltered, un-gay world where all I did was go to church and college, and moved to Los Angeles, four blocks away from West Hollywood.

At first, I was so filled with zealousness, I would let nothing be a stumbling block for me. But, then I realized I couldn't even go to the grocery store without having issues struggling with same-sex attraction. It really began to puzzle me, because the tools I had learned didn't seem to work in the real world. I started to get very frustrated and blamed myself. I got very depressed and ashamed. I went through a two-week phase of closeted drinking behind this Christian facade, because I was literally, overnight, the ex-gay poster teen. I was the John Paulk of the ex-gay teen generation. I was being pushed into leading the ex-gay youth movement. I was speaking to the Christian Coalition and the PFOX (Parents and Friends of Ex-Gays) conferences all over the country, and I didn't even know what was going on in my mind.

Then it just hit me, that although I did learn a lot of amazing things at Love In Action about character and behavior traits, I didn't want to go through this thing again, making destructive lifestyle choices. And it hit me, "Wade, your life was not destructive because you were gay. Your life was destructive because of the choices you were making." That light bulb went off and I knew I had to get out of there. "I can't do this. I'm not going to be caught in a big scandal—some ex-gay guy caught having homosexual relations."

I needed to get out of there. And I was starting to get lots of threats from the gay community, because of my involvement with Proposition 22 and the whole scandal with Dr. Laura. So, I figured the gay community really knows who I am here, and I'm really struggling because I want to go hang out in West Hollywood and find out what's going on down there, and I couldn't do that. So, I resigned from my position and moved back to Wisconsin.

I went to live with other ex-gays for a while. That was just a big mess. The unhealthiest choice I made. I was trying to live with these people who had not gone through a ministry like I had, so there were a lot of things I questioned in their lifestyle. One guy was obsessed with Mariah Carey and I thought for him to be saying he's a Christian, and changing his sexual orientation, that's a big no-no to be so infatuated with Mariah Carey. Those things started to bug me. Back when I was in L.A., I had a media debate on a Fox News program with Wayne Besen of the Human Rights Campaign. Wayne and I had this huge debate and, at the end, Wayne said to me, "Wade, when you decide that you're really gay, I want you to know that we're not going to reject you like the right wing will." So, to be a smart-ass, I told him that when he decided he wasn't a homosexual and admitted he was living in sin, we wouldn't reject him either. But, while I was in Maryland, I was an hour away from him. So, I wrote to him and let him know that I was dealing with some major issues.

What had happened was, I went to get an HIV test and the nurse saw me and said, "My goodness, you look so familiar. Aren't you that boy that was on *20/20*?" So, I told her that I was, and this total stranger said, "I just thought, if I ever saw that boy, I just wanted to let him know that he is okay and not to worry about who he is." It just hit me and I broke down in her office, just bawling. My life was just about to crack and this woman said that I was okay. That was it. That was really the straw that broke the camel's back. And I said to myself, "You know what? I *am* okay."

So, I talked to Wayne and ended up hanging out with him in D.C. and then I was supposed to have this huge coming out, flying into San Diego to do this massive coming out thing on MSNBC and Fox News. I wasn't ready for that, though, so Wayne told the *Advocate* that I was interested in coming out.

When I went into the Christian Coalition they taught me about what they called the non-sexual root causes of my sexual orientation. I thought, "Wow! You guys are so right! This is perfect." When I left, I felt so betrayed. I struggled that. They didn't tell me there were gay couples that had been together 20 years who have dedication ceremonies and live normal lives and have children. I didn't know that. I was naïve. I was friggin' 15 years old; what did I know about life?

When I came out in the *Advocate*, the vision for StandOut! came together. And that's where I am now. StandOut! has become a national gay and lesbian youth advocacy organization. Our goal is to get youth involved in their community, activism, and education. Right now, we're working on the Diversity and Discrimination Awareness Project. We've gotten all the contacts of the guidance counselors of the Alabama and Tennessee area, and we've given them information to host a diversity awareness day, where one of our members will come and speak at their school. It allows us to make contact with the schools, so that our members can start gay student alliances there.

We just had a new member join StandOut! and he's 20-years-old. He's a virgin. He has no doubts that he's gay, and he's never had anonymous sex with anybody, never had issues with having to find sex in a park or a bathroom. God, he's such a breath of fresh air to me.

There's a whole stereotypical lifestyle as a gay man, and that's why John Paulk and myself were so perfect for the movement. Everything they're saying that's negative about the gay community, we were. I'm a very rare case with the whole ex-gay thing. Not until recently have I spoken out about how I really feel about it. I did have a very good experience in it, but it's because I came from a very bad life experience. So, what I really needed was stability and I found that in a programmed setting; a structure.

The only people that I went through the program with who are still successful to this day are still involved with the program. Now they work for the program. And I think, as horrible as this sounds, "If you're so healed, why can't you go out in the real world? Because you know you're going to fall? That's not great comfort to the people you're trying to help."

I talk to so many people who went through the program with me who didn't graduate, who either had a "sexual fall" and got discharged or left on their own or who are still trying to live this double life. I have a really good friend who, bless his heart, continues to solicit gay sex in adult bookstores and public parks. He's trying to live this secret life. He said, "Wade, I wish I could come to the place where you are. You're comfortable with your homosexuality, and you don't view it as sin. It's just another issue in your life, like you have blonde hair." And I tell him all the time, "You've just got to get to that place. Your life is so destructive right now. How different are your sexual actions than mine? They're not, except that they are covered up and unhealthy, whereas mine are healthy, monogamous, and safe." And I'm finding unbelievable fulfillment. It breaks my heart. He left the ex-gay movement more disturbed, more guilt-stricken, and more ashamed than he was when he started. They're offering a false hope. They can't say it's freedom from homosexuality, because it's not. I struggled with the whole Christian thing and homosexuality thing, and I'm just so over it now. I look at my life now, and it's so fulfilling. My relationship is so pure. It's everything the Christian Coalition said would never happen and couldn't happen. And, honestly, sex used to be just a means for getting off. But now it's so intimate. I never had the best sex in my life until now. Now I know what it's all about. It's amazing how complete my life is. This ex-ex-gay poster-child thing—I hate that. I hate that more than anything. Just call me a youth advocate. ♣

UNDERGROUND *TRANSIT*

SCENE V, from a multi-part play

Kt Kilborn

[*The BLUE BOY opens the briefcase again and pulls out a blue suit jacket. Sending a prayer of thanks to Mother Butch herself, Peggy Shaw, he slips into the jacket. He first hums, then belts out the opening strain of Joni Mitchell's "Blue" as he straightens out his look.*]

Sharp, isn't it?
When I bought this suit,
I asked the tailor
I said,
"Hey man, don't worry about
offending me,
but,
do I look like a guy to you?"
He looked me up and down,
laughed a little
then said,
"Oh honey, not with those hips.
I'd still take you out."
Nah, no offense taken.
It's a damn fine suit, wouldn't you say?
I wore it one night with her,

and I was satisfied.
Except,
and this is the problem of the
feminist consciousness:
I woke up early the next morning,
my arm bridging the gap between the
swell of her hips
and the
curve of her breasts,
thinking.

I thought,
the world still knows
how much of a woman I am,
even if I'm not wearing
"three pieces of clothing
to match my sex."

I thought of Paula Martineau
and Georgia Langen:
two dykes imprisoned
after the death of Paula's young daughter.
It took the jury
seven years
to decide that her death
had been
an accident.

I wonder if Paula and Georgia
looked any
softer
after all that time.

There's a sharpness to a lesbian
I'm not decreeing
It's just what I've seen—

around the eyes—
it says
Fuck you.
I won't fit into the box
you created for me,
and if I must, I will not go
silently.
My eyes will speak for me
across the checkout line
on the porch of the house
with four kids.

I can't stand that silence.
It cuts me.
Paula and Georgia had it
but nobody sees it in me
without denying.

No, I am
short-haired self-confidence
I just ain't found the right guy
I'm a woman
confused
riding the night train through the Bronx
after all the kiosks close.

So when I woke up that dark morning
my girl's body pressed up against hers
I thought
we're in a different class
me and Paula and Georgia.
If it's not about money,
then it's about
passing.

You be the judge:
on my day in court
would you put me away?
Girlish tits and hips that
still look good in a
man's suit—
would you put this dyke away?

[*Opens shirt to reveal the ACE bandage that binds her breasts flat*]

What about this one?   [Train sounds]

I never thought I would say
I am beautiful.
I am hard-edged and tattoos
I am fast cars and guitars
I am hard for her when it excites us
and so, so soft
to her touch.

Paula, I would write it on my body
in sticky black letters
on some hard wall of my body
for you
if it would make any difference.
If it would make anybody see. ♣

FLESH COAGULATES

HERE

Tucker Lieberman

He prepares the skin to receive flesh. The condoms are nestled in an array of boxes and bottles, gleaming emollients, terrestrially colored cosmetic powder, fabric and flesh. What flights and fancies that linger in men's burning hearts will become flesh today?

Most people use latex as skin on living skin. He uses latex as skin on no skin, the skin that isn't skin but will become his skin, for he has no penis. It has nothing to do with a bed partner or whether he ever partners with anyone at all. It is about him alone, his monk flesh, his cloister skin, pure in his mind. He is constructing a body, he is constructing the part of his body he was born without, he is making a penis, he is filling a condom and wearing it, just for the record. I'll spoil the ending: he survives his life. There has been birdseed but it crunches and bumps the skin.

Feathers, yet the poor skin cannot fly. Honey pastes and clays harden into sharp edges and tear this helpless, unliving skin. Gels are decent but they eventually evaporate through the skin. Skin inside skin is just not right. What goes into skin today? What dust will become flesh today? River water in Providence and, at the other end of the train tracks, black sand from the

Boston harbor. Will they bubble in a shared cauldron? Rain water. Broccoli sprouts, black bean leaves. Mashed into paste for terrestrial testicles. And the trees that line the streets! Bark, roots, earth, wind. Divergent tapered elephant phalluses that open into sunlight, overgrown polished cobra stone in the twilight, yes, trees, bark, roots, earth, wind.

"Why would you want a tangled mess like a tree? Do you want that substance? Do you want that liability?" He stares at the trees, feels the coiled, pinched nerve in his belly, begging for extension. "Yes. I do. Give me that glorious tangled mess." Gaia constructs him a body. Today, all the world is his generation. It is snowing.

Snow, a meme, a singular entity, a collage of individual droplets with separate streamlined velocities rolling like windmills gathering moisture until they hit the ground. The space between the droplets, is that snow too? The water and the air go into the skin. Everything goes into the skin. Starlight rolls through the telescope and drips into the skin, the final seminal touch. He is sealing it with resin. He is laying it between burning white candles. He wears earphones instead of earmuffs. It is his favorite poem on the player. Gibran's Almustafa is considering, one more time, his departure from the land of his longing. He never tires of the story of this invisible star in the night hills who makes his journey between loneliness and ecstasies: "It is not a garment I cast off this day, but a skin that I tear with my own hands."

He feels a stirring in the dust between his legs. He is not only rooted to his princedom; his princedom is his root. The world is my phallus. I cannot leave, not for all the sand in the seas. ♣

IT'S HAPPY HOUR,

IT MUST BE . . .

MILLER TIME!

Rachel Kasa

Did you get what you wanted
when you gave everything else away?
Did you ever think you'd be happy
hiding behind a photograph in some industry publication,
in that halo haze of highlights
a panoramic panacea for passionate living?

There are thousands of others just like you,
caught in a pacific traffic jam
sunlight hits the outside-singing like a multitude
of believers,
but you never see it, do you?
Corridors lead only inside,
the deeper you are, the softer you fall.

When did you make the decision?
was it when you polished your face like a shiny resume,
and donned the funeral black,

1) Did they make the decision?
2) Did you let them?
3) Did you understand what they offered?

* Wages and Welfare
* Your Own Office
* Your Own Assistant

Yours truly,

_____

(your name here)

Your healthcare plan, your parking space, your X-mas bonus, your mortgage, your marriage, your menopause medication, your morning manicure, your caffeine, adrenaline, dopamine, viagra and 24-hour fitness addiction?

can you stand the ticking, the clock picking away
at
you,
that cab meter counting down
until you've slammed the door,
standing on the curb,
slapped by the street, the wind, and the hatred of
your own pretensions,
Too drugged to hear . . .
"take me, take me, take me
Out to the ball park—"
Ringing from your prison cell. ♣

BECOMING

sandra* Henderson

i am a statistic.
a portion of a percentage
and i
need to be analyzed
i need you to discover my roots
was it
how i was raised
or how i was born
what life experience
made me this way—was it a choice?
for some,
how can we change it
these abnormal statistics
these ridiculous labels
whose genetics could create this
queer, queer phenomenon
my answer MY answer
sits quietly deeper
i am who i
was made to be
stop creating me. ♣

I WAS A TEENAGE

BISEXUAL

Amy Bell

"It's not normal."

That was the reaction of my mother when the topic of homosexuality came up in conversation, before a recent stay in San Francisco. God only knows what she'd do if I told her I was bisexual. It's been easy, I guess, so far, because I've only really had "proper" relationships with men (she found that hard enough to deal with). Then again, I get the feeling she wouldn't even understand the concept of bisexuality. If I was heterosexual, she'd be proud that she's brought up a happy, healthy, "normal" child. Gay—yes, eventually, begrudgingly, she'd accept me. Bisexual? I don't think she'd even begin to comprehend.

Obviously, if I came out to my parents, the rest of my family would know about my bisexuality within 0.6 seconds flat. And even though I'm not exactly close to my aunts and uncles, cousins and grandma, I feel that somehow I'd become the black sheep, shunned along with my aunt (who got pregnant at 15 and ran off to live with a stranger on a houseboat). Soon I'd either fade into insignificance or, as the sole queer, become the target of unlimited scrutiny and opprobrium.

I have not come out yet; I have already anticipated the reaction from my family, and my peers. Up until twelve months ago, I attended a very exclusive, tuition-based private school; and I don't think I even need to explain how conservative that was. The school perceives itself as a moral, Christian institution, despite the huge number of Hindu and Muslim students—and therefore adheres to traditional Christian values. I imagine the faculty has barely discussed homosexuality; bisexuality isn't even on the radar. It was only the brave or foolhardy person who came out at my school. I heard of three "possible" queers during my entire eight years there and one of them was a teacher. To come out there would have been social suicide, and it wasn't as if my sexuality was any of their business anyway. It's not just parents and schoolmates I worry about coming out to. It's the rest of society, too. Everyone seems to think bisexuals are just going through a phase. Nowadays cool folks say experimenting with your sexuality is normal, but they believe girls like me just haven't figured out which one we are, straight or gay. The world may not be all black and white, but some people certainly want sexuality to be like that.

I admit, as a bisexual femme, I feel kind of ostracized by both gays and straights. Put it this way—with my lipstick, skirts and pocketbook, I don't look like what people imagine when they think "dyke." Yet the rabidly hetero meat market of nightclubs makes me want to puke. I'm caught between a rock and a hard place, between two "legitimate" sexualities, belonging to neither—or to both.

So, yeah, I like people of both genders. Well, of all genders, actually. I fall in love with the person, regardless of their external sexual organs. Why is that so difficult for some people to comprehend? I first realized I was bisexual two years ago, when I was 17. Staying my friend's house, unable to get to sleep one night, we decided to play Truth or Dare. He asked if I'd ever considered myself bisexual. Now, my sexuality was something I had wrestled with, but only in terms of either being purely gay or purely straight. I'd had sexual and romantic feelings towards the opposite sex since I was 10, towards the same sex since I was 11. I had heard the word "bisexual" in passing while reading biographies of Lou Reed and David Bowie, but never thought it could possibly apply to me. So I said "No," thought to myself, "That's a bit of a weird thing to be asking someone," and fell asleep soon after.

I thought no more of it until after I had received a letter from my friend in which he came out as bi, revealing to me that the only other person he'd told was his pen pal. I felt blessed to be allowed in on his secret. And it got me thinking. I knew I had the feelings; I couldn't deny them. So I put two and two together, and got, well, a four.

I am bisexual. Now where are my peeps? Where are the other bisexual youth? Adolescent crushes on members of the same sex are common, yet they're usually suppressed and put to the back of one's mind after, inevitably, petering out. In my local queer youth group, there are six gay guys, four lesbians and— guess what—no bisexuals of either gender (well, except me). And—but maybe this is just the company I keep—supposedly straight girls are always kissing other supposedly straight girls once they've had a bit too much to drink. Once they've sobered up, they all just return to Straightdom. Did the Sapphic shenanigans of the previous night mean nothing to them? Obviously not.

I lived and worked in San Francisco for a few months, and was astonished at the number of bi-oriented events and groups there were available. There were bi dance parties, bi discussion groups, bi coffee mornings, but all with one hitch; there were virtually no bisexuals under the age of 30. I mean, it was fantastic to find other kindred spirits, but it would have been even more fantastic if I could've found someone to empathize with me about the trials and tribulations of being a bi teen. Within such company, I often felt like—and often was—the baby of the group, despite being 19 and, therefore, technically an adult. It's particularly noticeable in the U.S. where I'm not old enough to legally drink and I'm refused entry to both gay and straight clubs. (Now just how symbolic is that?) Even back in the UK, where I live (and where I can drink legally) almost all the bis I know are 30—and

40-something. Only one friend, Gemma, is both bi and the same age as me. I'm not going to go on some mass-recruiting drive just because little ol' me feels lonely, but I'm sure there must be more bi teens out there. We need to raise our heads high if we want to show the world there's another option to gay and straight, and that it might even be better than those two. What's going to happen to bi-activism when all the current protagonists fighting for our rights are drawing their pensions? Clearly we need to join forces and make our voices heard if we want to make biphobia a thing of the past.

I guess I should start by walking my talk. I'm going to do my bit by coming out. I'm just starting my first year at university, where people are generally more lackadaisical about who is shagging whom and where, so who knows I might even find more bisexuals to take over the world with. Oops, did I just say that out loud? ♣

BRANDON IRON

Grover Wehman

My name is Brandon, Brandon Iron and I am
Man enough for me
Don't be deceived by the constructs of hair
The presence or absence of it determining my
Cock is not a hunk of flesh swelling and throbbing with desire
That you can see I
Think you should ask my girlfriend for a second opinion
One that as last night I was thrusting my
Iron cock inside her sweet cunt
Traveling beyond the biology book's definition of urethral sponge
    and labia beyond the
Greek term for vagina meaning sheath for a sword
But still her cunt was a home for my iron
And this boy who is sometimes a coal miner
Excavated the screams and her desire to feel my iron cock
Swelling and throbbing not much different than that of a
Real men don't strap on their dicks
Don't play with their clits
Don't bind down their tits and
Real girls don't either
But I am real enough for me
Girl enough you'll see
To be branding my iron when I was five
Pounding my clit not as if

My dick suddenly appeared when I paid toys in babeland in full
And showed my girlfriend my tool
Chest is full of pretty toys acquired from years of
Fucking with gender
My gender fucking started when I started fucking my gender
In my bedroom as a kid branding my tool
Chest is full of pride, way to go kid, she squirted all over your
    chest because it
Takes one to know one
My cock knows it has a cunt too
You've got to
Use what you've got my cunt tells my cock just where to
Rub her down tie her down tie me down I'm
Man enough to take it up the ass up my cunt
All fags welcome to brand my iron
Yes Sir, No Sir, I can take it Sir it's
Really not about taking it, but I like it like that so then well
Maybe it is
But that's not really what makes me a man,
It has nothing to do with taking it, my Iron and how I brand it
I brand me . . .
Deep and scarred
My cunt my soul
Hey girl
Doesn't live here anymore
Never did but yes she is
Still here just hurt and hiding because she has never really been
    wanted by my body
Wanted by my
Mother wanted a girl
Wanted to love this girl that was never really here
But now she is branded by my
Facial hair and underwear aren't really hiding anything that can't
    be found out by just asking those questions I have been
    asking myself for fourteen years as I have been branding my
    iron since I was five

Branding my iron and hoping to find
By branding my iron I am branding iron I am
Brandon Iron
Nice to meet you ♣

DIRTY SECRET (BEING A LESBIAN SUNDAY SCHOOL TEACHER)

Alicia Brooks

"So, guess what I do on Sunday mornings now? What would you really *not* expect me to do on a Sunday morning?" This is how I begin a conversation I like to call my second coming out. I came out as a lesbian when I was 16. Now, at 22, I am coming out as a Sunday school teacher.

Yes, for the past six months, I have been waking up at the crack of dawn each Sunday to read Bible stories and sing songs with 22 extremely energetic first and second graders. This comes as quite a shock to most people. At least in my hometown, one doesn't come across many beer drinking, tattooed, skirt chasing Sunday school teachers. I don't embody many of the qualities one associates with Sunday school. I'm not meek or conservative or even particularly pious. My friends aren't used to hearing me say "God" without following it up with "damn." When I told one friend about my new Sunday morning activity, she stared in silence for a good minute before stammering, "Alicia, do you even believe in God?" My boss even envisioned me teaching Tom Waits-style: sitting at a piano, drink in hand, murmuring things like "Kids, let me tell you why women are nothing but trouble."

So how did I wind up with this job? I attended Sunday school and church with a Methodist congregation from the age of three through high school. I loved it as a child and I remained a very devout Christian through about the tenth grade. By the time I was 16, though, much had changed. I still agreed with the basic tenets of Christianity. Yet, as I came to understand myself as a liberal, feminist dyke, I began to feel distant from my more conservative congregation. I knew God didn't mind that I kissed girls, but I was unsure of how everyone else in church would feel. I was not yet confident enough to assert my identity within the church, so I drifted away and only attended church on a sporadic basis during college. After I graduated and moved back home, I realized that I missed church. I also missed working with young children, something I had done in school. One morning, as I was musing on these two holes in my life, my mother mentioned that our church was desperate for Sunday school teachers. The coincidence seemed provident. I casually mentioned that I might be interested, forgetting that churches and mothers are the most efficient gossip networks on earth. Within 24 hours, I received a phone call from the very harried Sunday school superintendent begging me to volunteer. I took a risk and agreed.

A week later, I nervously attended my first planning meeting, a host of disastrous possibilities swimming through my head. I was certain that an alarm would go off when I entered the room, signaling the presence of a sinner. At minimum, I knew that at least one of the other teachers would be a crazy Bible-thumper obsessed with the breakdown of family values. Thankfully, my fears proved to be unfounded. When I walked in, I received a friendly greeting from the other teachers, none of whom seemed particularly scary. Then, just as I was starting to relax, the strangest thing happened. The superintendent pointed to a closet in the back of the room and explained that we could go there if we needed scissors, glue, or markers. Then, as a joke, she added

"Or if you need to lock a kid in the closet . . . Or lock yourself in the closet . . . Or come out of the closet." Everyone else laughed, so they didn't notice me looking up at the ceiling, wondering if I had just received God's first-ever divine segue.

This was not the only time during the meeting that I sensed my differences from everyone else. At one point, we discussed the year's calendar, planning various seasonal activities. When we got to February, the superintendent talked about making valentines for a nursing home. She was ready to move on, when I raised my hand and asked, "What about Black History Month?" Minutes later, she was saying "There really isn't anything in March," when I interrupted, "Women's History month!" Some of the other teachers seemed a bit surprised by my suggestions, but they still added them to the calendar. I left the meeting with a growing sense of the impact that I could have on a Sunday school program. Six months later, I'm still not out in Sunday school. My students have no reason to know anything about my personal life and the topic has not come up with my fellow teachers. I don't try to hide it, though. I keep the pink triangle button on my backpack when I carry it to class. If I had a girlfriend, I would bring her to church with me. Thus far, however, my queerness is a not an issue and I feel no need to make it one. Instead, I am subversive in more subtle ways. I taught a lesson on how God gave everyone families—all different and all special. Another lesson was about being everyone's friend, even if someone seems very different from you. As part of my lesson on Noah and the Arc, I had my class make rainbow magnets, symbolizing God's promise to Noah in the story. (My friends got a serious kick out of that one.)

While regular teachers may be part of your life for only a year or so, Sunday school teachers tend to stick around for decades. Many of my own Sunday school teachers remain part of our church community, and thus they're a part of my life to this day. This affords them the opportunity to become true role models, mentors, and trusted friends. I am able to see them as real people and observe how they take part in the larger community of the church. It is in this capacity that I hope I can really impact my students. While I may never have occasion to come out to my second graders, I hope that we all remain part of the same church community for years to come. By watching me live my life openly and honestly, I hope they can see that there is more than one way to be a woman and a Christian.

Of course, I also hold on to the fantasy that ten years from now one of my students will be sitting with his Gay/Straight Alliance buddies in a high school cafeteria musing, "I think my Sunday school teacher was gay, too!" ?

MY REAL WORLD:

A LETTER

Matt Swanson

Dear Diane,

I wanted to send you a quick note on my real world, about "real" gay life. I don't mean what you see on MTV's *Real World* or *Queer as Folk*. I'm talking LIFE, as I know it anyway. Not that those Babylon boys aren't hot or anything, but that's exactly my point. Gay guys put so much emphasis on how we should look and act. I can't think of how many dozens of times I've looked at myself in the mirror and wondered what kind of man could ever find me attractive. That makes life difficult. Not that life doesn't have its good times—because it does. But if you let it, gay life can be a real kick in the pants.

The biggest obstacle for me to overcome, aside from just being queer, is being disabled. I am visually impaired. I have no sight in my left eye and partial sight in my right eye. I have glaucoma and I was born with congenital cataracts. Because of all this, my field vision is greatly reduced. In school, I have to sit in the front row to read the chalkboard, and sometimes even then I can't see it. I also need to use large print textbooks, and prefer to have handouts enlarged as well. Most people, upon finding out that I cannot drive, automatically assume that I am helpless. That can be hard to deal with, and I'm still learning how to cope. I have never allowed my disability to defeat me, but it does really affect my body image. I wear thicker then typical glasses, which tend to make me look, well in all honesty, ugly.

Body image is such a weakness for me. I guess it is for other 17-year-olds too. I spend so much time trying to look my best, I often forget to have fun and experience life. Many people have told me I shouldn't worry so much. Heck, I've even had a few boys tell me I'm quite attractive. But for some reason I can't shake the feeling of not living up to the fashion standards. What makes things worse is that I've never dated a man. Is it any wonder I feel inadequate?

Still, I have found so much security and safety by being out to people. That may sound odd, but I have had such a chance to get to know other queer youth and that has been great. I went to my first pride festival last summer, and it was the most incredible event I've ever attended. I ended up getting interviewed on prime time news, outing myself to half the city and loving every minute of it. I love getting a chance to express myself. Anyway, there it is, my spewing of thoughts. I hope it makes sense.

Love, Matt ♣

THE REBEL SONG

Holden Jude Dean

I'm a high school beauty queen
And a Noxema princess
I'm the new gaunt Gap teen
With my daddy's girl excess
I'm a *Seventeen* magazine activist
Badass straightedge chic
I spout candy-coated politics
Aren't I just so unique?
Chorus I'm the next hard-core backdoor superstar
Got a plastic bad girl repertoire
I'm the new age old-school poster child
I drive all those preteen rebels wild
I've got my Zach de la Roca shrine
I'm the angriest kid in school
Perfected my Zach de la Roca whine
'Cause communism's so damn cool
I'm in a constant state of suicide
Got a therapist standing ovation
I wear my fucked up with pride

And my anti-angst medication
Chorus I've got upper middle class
Fastcash backlash
And that tragedy
Maybelline stock crash
I've got pain in all the fall colors
Even no name brand hot rollers
But I can take it all
To the next level
I'm a wet dream front-page rebel ♣

BEFORE

THE TRANSITION:

MY ADVICE

Kristin

After months of counseling, sorting through loads of family issues, and plenty of soul searching, I recently started transitioning from life as a man to life as a woman. After pushing myself through this agonizing process I am looking forward to the changes that lie ahead. I also find myself in the unusual position of having some advice to offer up to people who find themselves in the same situation. I have collected some reflections on things that a young transgendered person should give thought to before starting down the road to transition. Here they are, in no particular order:

1. Getting Ready: This whole transsexual issue is dirty business and it's very demanding. Before you move to actively transitioning, you really need to be sure you have what it takes. As a younger person you're putting yourself at a gigantic risk because of your lack of rights. So the first and most certain thing is this, you have to be ready to lose everything—friends, family, access to higher

education, and most of your creature comforts. You have to be ready to feel the sometimes-overwhelming emotions, to comb all the parts of your life. Is this to say everyone will have a hellish time Transitioning young? Luckily, most people's Transition lies somewhere between a walk in the park and walk in the seventh circle of hell. The single most complicated issue for a transgendered person to deal with at any age is family and to a lesser degree, friends. You must take extreme caution when telling your parents. Even outwardly liberal people can take this news poorly, especially at first. It's one thing to support alternative life styles in the conceptual sense; it's a different issue completely when it is resides in their own home. Also, you need to remember: it is all about them. Parents will wonder about their parenting skills, be scared about what other people think, be afraid of what their child's life will be like. These feelings can all be compounded for your same sex parent. Fathers are often not excited to find out their little boy really feels like a girl. You'd be wise to consider the amount of information you give people at one time; don't overwhelm them with the details of hormone replacement therapy when first they need to know what a transsexual is.

2. Education and Your Future: Remember that you risk your education and your future if the worst-case scenario comes to pass. You must not let pain blind your judgment; your education shouldn't be sacrificed. That's right, I am saying that you should hold off on transitioning until you have that all important college degree, if your parents might react in a horrible way. Because once you're in college there's stuff you can do anyway. Start seeing a psychiatrist now, and you could set yourself up for a quick transition right after college. You could even work on stuff like voice lessons while you're still there, perhaps block that nasty androgen (or estrogen). If you do tell your parents or other people you need to stay calm. You may feel anger at their

less-then-open-armed reception, that's typical. Although it might be all about you, you need to avoid taking that attitude when dealing with your family and friends. Avoid being belligerent or pushing too much on them at one time. Don't be afraid to argue a little, but don't take it personally. Stay happy and helpful, try to be extra good to your family. The more you help them bear their own crosses, the more likely they are to help you bear your own. Dealing with the emotional ups and downs of transitioning without a support network is a mistake.

3. Emotions, Reflection, and Locking In: Your emotions are a double-edged sword. You can't block them out, because emotions tend to be all or nothing. When I started to "feel" again, beyond the blahs of depression, it was very overwhelming. My first reaction was to try to gain complete control over them. This doesn't work, you end up shutting out certain emotions and causing more problems later. Deal with everything as it comes, feel it all; love, pain, hatred, self-loathing, confusion, exhalation, fear, courage, despair and hope. Each has their place in the balance of things, neither block nor dwell on any of them. Reflection on one's life is in my view a near necessity when dealing with being transsexual. Many people, plenty that I've met at least, lock in on the goal of transition. Accordingly they lock in on parts of their own life that validate this goal. However, it would be a very bad idea to not look at the whole scope of your life. To assume that a 100 percent of the pain, suffering, and issues of your childhood will go away by transitioning is just not true. There are far too many transgendered folks with self esteem and body image issues. Why is this? Because they bury the other issues that come up from their old lives. When people fixate on something so completely, they often neglect other areas.

A damaging and unique effect of "locking in" for young adults has to do with growing up. If all your energies and thought go into transitioning, then they can't be going anywhere else. For example, that might mean working extra hours while in college, so you can start saving for gender reassignment surgery, but because you have no time, you have to forgo the "college experience." Choices like this prove unhealthy, as those years are fundamental in personal exploration and development. Another dreadful issue is when young adults have no goals other than transitioning. It's easy to get locked into gender reassignment surgery to the point of having a gigantic hole in our lives so that when we finally transition, we find ourselves with no further goals in life. It is like, "What now?

4. Why Transition: Being a women? Being yourself? I messed with this a lot. What's your goal in transitioning? Is it to be the perfectly passable female? To sound like, verbalize like, flirt like, a women? In short, are you jumping from one stereotype into another? Don't fool yourself; while there is real a biological difference between male and female brains, it's not to the point of a chauvinist view of women. The whole reason you are transitioning is to be yourself. Not to be some cardboard cut out that society has made for you. My last point is more an observation and piece of personal experience than anything else. I learned a difficult lesson about transitioning: that doing it during young adulthood only magnifies it. Transitioning is about figuring out who you are and so is adolescence. So we start from scratch and, for me, this means once again muddling around, trying to find myself. Will I really still care about sports, computers, gaming, and a myriad of other things? It can be really scary not knowing yourself well. Don't allow this fear to make you take on yet another false identity or stereotype just for the sake of having one. My advice is to let go, and just be. Because the rest has a way of falling into place when you let go and live. ♣

FOR MCKINLEY

Holden Jude Dean

I want you dressed in nothing
But your eyes
With their cobalt innocence
Your hands encircling mine
As the world spins
Much too quickly and
I can't hold on
And in your mouth
There are endless dawns
Each more burning scarlet
And damaging
Than the next
Oh god
I've lost myself again
In the smoke white softness
Of your skin
The porcelain
I keep screaming
Deaf on my own ears
Happily blind I'll just
Ignore the bodies
On your shore.

Such a beautiful death
It will be.
Shipwrecked
Upon you.
I have to save myself
This is going to kill. ♣

THE TRAGIC BALLAD

OF JILL AND BOBBY

Meredith Matthews

Bobby and Jill went down to the store
To buy bread for their dear sweet Mama
But they ran into a roadblock
It seemed that they were stuck
And this is what they saw
They saw-
Dykes on bikes and Fags on trikes and
Chicks with dicks and big headlights
Dorothy and Toto were there that day when
Jill and Bobby saw the Pride Parade

Well then Jill and Bobby ran home to tell Mommy
Of the crazy things that they'd seen and heard
Mom sat there and listened
A tear of laughter glistened
But she did not say a word

About the-
Mama said, "I'd forgotten what the day was today
I should not have allowed you to go
But did you see your Aunt Ida
From South Carolina
Who used to be your Uncle Joe?
Among the-

Now since then small Jilly went on to high school
And she moved on to the head of her class
Then she joined the Marines
Became Captain Josephine
And tells no one when nobody asks

Now as Jilly was blowing things up all around
With expensive government bombs
Bobby tried on Mom's dresses
And grew out his tresses
And he crimped and he curled
And he dabbed and he whirled
And he twirled and he looks like a girl
He lives in New York with some guy named Stefan!
Poor mama she lives all alone nowadays
The husband she loved now is dead
She does not blame this mess
On some queer culture excess
All she wanted was a damn loaf of bread. ♣

DANNY'S

ANNOUNCEMENT

Meredith Matthews

I prefer all my clothes to have crotches
And pockets and collars
I try to stand "just right" in my 501s
And try to affect cool disinterest
Even if leaning against my wallet just threw my back out
I shine my Doc Martens and wear them with everything
People sometimes call me "sir" on the phone
And in person
And I walk with more bounce than my mother would prefer
And I never have a bad hair day
Just bad haircuts
I rise when a Lady stands to do whatever it is that
Ladies spend hours in
the bathroom doing
I hold doors for everyone
Even the perplexed-looking guys
I feel alone more than I would like to
And smoke more than I should
I don't dance very well
But I'm great at pool
And a couple of silly bar tricks that make everyone laugh

I'm a musician, an artist, and a computer genius
And a Pisces and a zydeco music fan and a
long-walks-beneath-the-stars type
And I will never admit that I do this just to meet
Women
I stand apart from the crowd, usually on the crowd's own volition
I do what feels right and good for me
And I don't give a good goddamn how uncomfortable
that makes anyone
Because I feel
        I just feel
And that's a great thing to know how to do
If you never learned before
When I'm sad, I cry
When I'm happy, I laugh
When I'm scared, I fight back
And when I'm with the Woman I love,
She places her happiness into my hands
And offers her tenderest parts into my mouth
And I feel her blossom into my empty places
Complete, she lets me guide her to the screaming edge
Where we are happy to remain
I am her boitoy
Not her man
And she wants me that way
I may be my own woman
But
I'm her butch ♣

MY INNER

HAIRDRESSER

(Is an Anti-Capitalist Dyke): A Manifesto

Anissa Weinraub

Whenever I travel to another part of the U.S. or another country I find myself taking on the speech patterns of a native speaker. I lose my own way of speaking, and adopt that area's accent. I am an Accent Chameleon. I find it a fun little linguistic/sociological game. This summer I worked in a restaurant deep in the heart of Dupont Circle in Washington D.C., an area known far and wide for its dense Guppie (gay male, yuppie) population. Eighty percent of the staff was gay, so it seemed only natural that I should adopt the Guppie mode of communication, behavior, and self-representation.

I was a Sexual Identity Gender Expression Chameleon. SIGEC, for short.

Okay, I became a gay boy. It was a sociological extrapolation. After all, who doesn't simply adore another acronym in their life?

My demeanor changed; I incorporated that flipping of the wrist thing, my body developed a certain poise, as I flowed gracefully, melodramatically from room to room. I oozed sass.

And to uphold just a few more stereotypes about gay male culture of the modern century, it was during this SIGECian period of my life when I first discovered my inner hair dresser.

It started with a minor compulsion to do hair. I found myself spending more time than ever staring into the mirror, strategically situating each strand. It quickly escalated, infecting the realm of my desire: I wanted to cut hair. Mine, my housemate's, that guy who walked by me in the park and so desperately needed a solution for his mullet. Anyone. I found myself nightly snipping off different pieces of hair, my wastebasket mounding with black, brown, and bleached little trimmings, the cast-offs of my art.

I became irked easily when people paid $9.99 for a shoddy Super Cuts 'do. I became restless, itching to conquer hairdos of all genres. Strolling on busy streets, I was a *flaneur*, constantly taking in the hairstyles moving past me. In the supermarket, I insatiably devoured the hair concepts sprouting atop all the shoppers. I was a machine, always, everywhere calculating length and luster, shade and sheen and type of sheers used. I had undergone a pop-cultural metamorphosis, emerging from my cocoon a hair person.

For me, there was always a stigma attached to the label of "hair person." I mean, I'm not the shallow, valley-girl type. I don't maniacally rush out to buy the latest *Cosmo* or *Elle* or *Teen People* so as to bask in the beauty that is Gwenyth Paltrow or Jennifer Anniston or the entirety of Destiny's Child's new 'dos, in pure awe of the shine or cut or angulation of those soft, wispy bangs, wildly ecstatic over all the new hair-ideas it presents me, wholly satiated like a hypoglycemic devouring a Kit Kat bar. That's just not me.

I mean, I'm that rabid feminist, always managing to work a radical critique of capitalism or patriarchy into every conversation. I'm that crunchy little dyke with unshaven legs and armpits, always shrieking about the image-of-women-in-the-media and those-fascist-beauty-standards that consume women's lives as they quite literally kill themselves off in order to attain them. I'm that dirty kid who lives in a coop, a little Luddite denouncing the evils of

American consumerism while eating organic tofu and alfalfa sprouts.

A hair person? Certainly not me.

But like so many other components in my life, hair simply needed to be re-appropriated. And, not unlike those faux-poetic Calvin Klein waifs, or Jewel, I like to embrace my contradictions.

Sometimes it's not even about the hair on my head. Sometimes "doing hair" is much more of a conceptual art. Grappling with what really constitutes a "style." Is it based solely on outcome, precision? Does intent matter? Is it realized within the space between conception and production? It can easily bust into a discourse on the essence of hair.

Sometimes it's just the time spent with myself. A moment of pause, for reflection or affirmation. Some people do yoga or bake vegan chocolate pies or legally gamble in the stock market. I do hair.

I do hair.

I can reach a state of self-awareness, a tweaked less-about-the-greatness-of-the-world-more-about-the-greatness-on-my-head mindfulness. There's an almost Zen head space that exists in a 3 a.m. touch-up of the strands on the back of my head that I've never really seen, only sensed.

There is such strength attained in personal transformation, in the ability to carve out, trim up, or buzz off some new identity. Better than a self-help book, taking the sheers into your own hands is a momentous step toward self-sufficiency.

It cuts the obligatory ties between you and an Imperial Barber Force; no longer must you rely on some superior entity that controls the wealth of hair expertise. Yours is an act of the redistribution of knowledge, an act of revolution. When you pick up that hammer and sickle, don't forget some sheers and a comb. Two examples:

The Hair Moment: As in, going up to a stranger with a style you adore, envy, or simply want to emulate: "Let's have a Hair Moment. What do you do?" Pure De Tocquevillean communitarian principles in action; it is participatory citizenship.

The Hair Moment has the potential to bridge the gap between strangers. It facilitates the transition from blindly sharing the streets with dark figures, anonymous forms, to sharing great hair tips with a new friend. But even more than just a pizza night product-swap on the kitchen table or a public restroom quickie session of "gotta-tries" or "stay-away-froms," the Hair Moment takes the form of two strangers quickly uniting as they share their processes of etching out their individual Hair Personas. It can forge the link between individuals who have forgotten about their fellow mammal, so accustomed to interacting only with cold technology, or commuting for hours in an isolated little car on a mega-highway from an unfriendly home to a dehumanizing work. The Hair Moment can restore society's hope in itself.

Triangulation Method: The tour de force of my hair-cutting repertoire, the Triangulation Method incorporates both shortening and thinning in a series of blunt chops made somewhat randomly. Its utilization of varied angles of scissor-approach creates a textured, multi-lengthed, kinda-spunky style.

I was once explaining Triangulation to someone who happened onto my porch-stoop-turned-beauty-parlor. I described the Method with zealous detail and emphatic hand gestures; launching the epic tale, complete with an exposition of eerie foreshadowing, an incremental augmentation of the dramatic tension, finally reaching the hair climax, and ending with a swift, yet settling denouement. I must say, one of my finer Hair Moments. But she just rained on my parade, with a flat, "Oh, like spiking."

Well, excuse me. But, in order to make it in a world in which you're implicitly told that your vote doesn't really count all that much, that your identity can easily be marginalized by the powers that be, or that your struggles and movements for changing the system can be squashed by the Asymmetrical Warfare existing under democratic martial law (we're armed with guns, all you've got are those silly puppets) . . . In order to just make it through the day, breathing and laughing and ready to take on another, you need a little inflation. You need to feel sublime, majestic, and even invincible about something. Like you have an irresistible offering to the world. Even if it is meager by some essentialist standard of value.

Even if it is cutting hair. ♣

EXHIBITIONIST

MODESTY AT THE

NUDE BEACH

Holden Jude Dean

Today my skin is as thin as cigarette paper
And I still falter when I ask her name
Because we're not the same
No matter how much the bible
Tells me so

Because I've got sand under my nails
And the child in my smile
Still shows through sometimes
So I walk away and help
The toothless Spanish women find
Tin can treasure, in the sand

They seem to understand me
Muttering sí, señora and
Toddling away through miles
Have wrinkled cock and balls
The water here can be a mirror
If you look hard enough
But I can't walk on it

No no, because I don't have
Six legs or a crucifix and
Neither do the other heretics
But they seem content to fake it ♣

HOW MANY GENDERS

FIT IN A WOMEN'S

COLLEGE?

Tucker Lieberman

"I hoped to meet women who I could identify with," recalls Daniel Soltis, an FTM who attended Pennsylvania's all-women college Bryn Mawr. "I learned to be a feminist and a radical and an activist. . . . I worked on a feminist newspaper and started drawing comics about being queer and female. I got a women's symbol tattooed on my arm, embroidered 'Lesbian' onto my backpack."

Daniel is just one of the many female-to-male transgendered people (FTMs) who find themselves drawn to life at an all-women's college. There are a variety of reasons for this fast-growing trend—many hope to find acceptance for their gender expression in a supportive, progressive, female environment—but sometimes it's a difficult path to take.

The term "transgender" encompasses all forms of gender variance, which may include dress, mannerisms, or surgical reassignment. Not all transgendered people seek to live full-time as a member of the opposite sex. People increasingly claim third-gender identities, including "genderqueer" and "boi." When one considers the range of possible gender identities and the larger number of possible journeys to get there, it is not astonishing that some people born female might wind up at a women's college somewhere along the way, even if "woman" is not a complete description of their gender identity.

Daniel, a Bryn Mawr alumnus, saw a "wide variety of different gender expressions" at college and felt that his gender expression was normal within that context. "Which is probably why being FTM didn't occur to me [in college]. It was this environment where, even though I was lacking the words at the time, I could easily be a boy and be a woman at the same time."

He identified as "butch" while at college and began transitioning from female to male a couple years after graduation. One of the comics on his website CoyoteComics.com features a goateed FTM who returns to a lesbian's group he was active in before he transitioned. The character reminisces on how there had once been a question of whether to include bi women and makes an analogy to the group's current debate about whether to include FTMs.

In retrospect, Daniel questions whether the lack of a supportive, diverse environment would have pushed him to transition earlier, or whether the perpetuation of that environment would have made his transition unnecessary. In any case, he is happy that he has transitioned and writes proudly of his college experience.

Daniel's explanation of the appeal of a women's college is echoed by Ellie Graham, a senior at Wellesley College in Wellesley, Mass. Ellie, originally from Louisville, Kentucky, is transgendered and doesn't identify as either a woman or a man.

He believes that many FTMs choose to attend women's colleges because "there's a space to have more than one gender," recalling how one student observed that Wellesley had "boys and girls, but they were all girls." Students are defined by how they choose to present themselves, rather than by their biology, which is an attractive culture for many transgendered people.

As the president of Peer Resources, Ellie coordinates the training of student counselors. In Fall 2003, he brought a speaker who left Smith after starting to transition from female to male. Ellie recalls that, in his junior year, the college's Center for Work and Service hosted a panel devoted to transgender issues. The transgendered students on campus began to develop community with the arrival of an older, vocal, undergraduate FTM.

The 'T' was added to the acronym of Wellesley's queer student organization (WLBTF, pronounced "We'll Be Tough") by the time Ellie arrived on campus, and it was at Wellesley that he first heard the word "transgendered" and began to accept his gender identity. "I think the organization is starting to be more aware, to serve that need, and make the campus more aware [of transgender issues]."

Ellie perceives that Wellesley's bathroom policy accommodates transgendered students well. In the past, Wellesley dorms voted either to restrict their bathrooms to females at all times or to permit people of other genders who knock first. Now, the trend is for dorms to vote either to restrict their bathrooms to Wellesley students at all times or to permit non-students who knock first. The transgender students are pleased with this arrangement, but it is only beginning to be seen as a transgender initiative, says Ellie. A more common justification of the Wellesley-only limitation is that students are bound by the college's honor code to respect other students.

Ellie knows only one FTM who is currently seeking transition. Before he became aware of that person, he said, "We don't want to press the issue [of acceptance of transition] until we know that the administration would be favorable. It's better to have nothing than to have something bad passed." The issue of transition has since been raised to the administration.

Professor of Mathematics Helen G. Grundman, who has been at Bryn Mawr College since 1991, is a genetic woman who's been involved in the transgendered community for eight years. She recalls that when students founded the Gender Liberation Organization in the spring of 2000, one of their main goals was to increase the presence of transgender issues in the curriculum, including the possibility of an entire course devoted to the subject. The group was aware of an FTM student who planned to transition and they sought to influence administrative policies that affect transgendered people. (That student ended up transferring to a co-ed college.)

Grundman said, "If a young trans has, in the past, found a lot of support in the lesbian community for his masculine gender expression . . . and a lot of rejection from others, it makes all the sense in the world that he may choose to go to a women's college, particularly one that is believed to have a strong queer community."

It is important, say many FTMs, to see the difference between finding support in the lesbian community and personally identifying as a lesbian. "I never wanted to look like a butch dyke," says Ness, an 18-year-old freshman at Cedar Crest College in Allentown, Pennsylvania. Ness (an androgynous form of his given name) began his "gender discovery" in his senior year of high school in Stratford, Connecticut, when he began to try to pass as a man.

He originally believed it wouldn't matter to him if he attended a women's school since he'd be in women's dorms wherever he went. Later he realized that many co-ed colleges help transgendered students find dorms consistent with their identities. Choosing a women's college "turned out to be the hard way, gender-wise."

Ness identifies as transgendered, tolerates either pronoun, is seeking a new gender-neutral name, and is not interested in medical transition. "It's really more of a social and personal view of 'boys' and 'girls' that sort of gets me. I like the social standing of being a boi." He thinks it would be awkward to transition while living on campus but he makes an effort to pass as a man when he is off campus with friends. He also identifies as polyamorous and is currently involved with several people of both sexes.

Ness knows only one other FTM. "I've got friends who understand, but as for [knowing] others with personal experience [of being FTM], I don't really have too many people to talk to." He says he has been reluctant to reach out to strangers for support since even his friends can't always identify with what he's going through.

Jackie Bolduc, president of OutThere, the gay student group at Cedar Crest, is dating an FTM who attends the Art Institute of Philadelphia. She also has several FTM friends, and so for her, "trans issues are both political and personal." Bolduc is planning a transgender awareness day where she hopes to correct misperceptions about transgendered people. She gained the idea after attending the University of Delaware's trans awareness week in April 2003 where Leslie Feinberg spoke.

Simmons College in Boston recently brought Jennifer Finney Boylan, professor of English at Colby College and a male-to-female transsexual, to read from her new memoir *She's Not There*. Many people in the audience were transgendered. They included Stone (one name, thanks, like Madonna and Jesus) who has been an employee of Simmons since September 2003. His co-workers call him by his legal, feminine name, but students perceive him as a man. Stone has found that Simmons' queer groups for students and for faculty and staffs are inclusive of transgendered people.

Not everyone is able to find space at a women's college—and sometimes the women's college can't find space for them. Matt, who was the president of the queer student organization at Lesley College in Cambridge, Mass., was asked to leave when the administration learned of his plan to transition.

Matt transferred to Lesley in Fall 2000 as a sophomore. He was androgynously identified at the time he arrived, but soon he began to "explore" and to transition genders "socially and spiritually," preferring male pronouns. He was the president of the queer alliance that year, running events and bringing FTM speakers to campus.

In the summer of 2001, he legally changed his name to Matthew. The administration asked him to clarify the situation when he returned to school. Matt—who felt he was androgynous looking at the time, but not yet passing as a man—explained his transition. A week later, the administration told him they had made a decision: he was not welcome at the women's college if he didn't represent himself as a woman.

"I felt that there was something shameful I had done to cause this disruption, because I didn't know how to talk about it without feeling upset," he said. "I felt like I had a contagious disease. I consider myself a really peaceful person, and there was so much fear around me."

He finished the semester at Lesley College, the women's college at Lesley University, and accepted the offer of a permanent spot at Lesley's co-ed Adult Baccalaureate College. The co-ed college did not provide housing, offered classes mostly on weekends, and there were many working parents in the student body—a much different undergraduate experience than Matt had planned for himself.

Janet Schulte, Dean of Lesley College, says, "I do not recall that Lesley University took any formal action to ask Matthew to leave Lesley College for the Adult Baccalaureate College. I do know that Matthew did leave Lesley College and enrolled in ABC, but it was by Matthew's own volition."

Ironically, as a Lesley University student, Matt was still able to enroll in women's studies classes at the women's college, where the professors called him by his preferred name and masculine pronouns.

"My mom was very supportive of me," he said. His mother had also attended Lesley's co-ed college. "But we also didn't know what to do, because our personal opinion was going up against this huge school."

Matt knew other FTMs at the women's college and wished they would come out and support him, but, he says, they were afraid that they would be expelled. When the administration asked Matt for their names, he refused.

He began taking testosterone in his senior year. Despite the fact that he had been a well-liked campus celebrity for his activism regarding gender and sexual identity, he gradually felt alienated from his former community. Some members of the gay student organization seemed angry that Matt had been such an active president and suddenly left; others, in his absence, questioned why a transgendered man had ever been president of a lesbian group to begin with.

Matt chose not to publicize the issue until after graduation, an event that he did not attend. "I had done so little to make them unhappy, and I was already so deep into the situation, that I did not want to make it into a huge media deal."

The most notable thing about transgendered students at women's colleges is that their motives are just like everyone else's. They aren't there for transgender politics or publicity. They want a supportive environment with women who understand, and they want the freedom to be themselves.

When asked why he chose Lesley College, Matt explained, "I wanted to go to a women's college because I wanted a feminist perspective in my major, counseling and psychology. I also thought people would understand and relate more about social pressures."

Unfortunately, transgendered people—who have extreme discomfort fitting into traditional gender roles—often feel that masculine behavior and identity are not permitted to them while they are in women's space. They fear rejection and even expulsion. But as women and transgendered people live, work, and study together, and allow each other space to be themselves, it may become apparent that the gender differences that define them need not divide them. ♣

Section Three

[FAMILY, FRIENDS, CHOICES]

FAGGOT

R.L. Baldwin

You just don't know how much I love my brother. I wish he would come on, though. He said he was getting out of choir practice at five and since momma and pops bought us one car to share, I gotta wait for him. I hope he can't smell this weed on me. He don't really like when I smoke. My brother is a good boy. He ain't never smoke or drink with me and all the fellas. Not even a Newport. I used to think he was still a virgin but now I know better.

My brother is one of the smartest niggas I know. He know how to dress, he think he can play ball, and he wants to be a psychologist 'cause he always wanna talk to people and know what they are thinking. I know one day he will be one of them know-it-all professional acting counselors on Ricki Lake or Jenny Jones trying to talk some sense into some ghetto-ass girl with 10 babies by 11 different men. A lot of people say we act just alike. And we do in a lot of ways. We like the same music, like the same TV shows, borrow each other clothes and we look just alike. We *are* twins. Identical. Born September 16, 1984.

My brother is my heart. I was born two minutes before him and momma says I have been looking after him every since. Momma loves to tell the story 'bout when we were just six or seven and some boy took my brother's Garbage Pail Kids cards. My brother just ran home crying but I beat the dude up, made him give the cards back and then went to his house with him and took his cards to give to my brother. I know we the same age but I always felt like a big brother to him. Somebody at our school fuck with him they know they got to deal with me. But everybody at our school like my brother Trent. (I'm Travis by the way.) Some niggas like him too much. That the only problem I have with my brother.

You see, Trent think he gay. Even though we tight and talk about everything, I don't know if he ever was gonna tell me about it. The only reason I know is one day I walked in on him and that grown ass nigga David that live around the corner fucking or whatever faggots do. I'm sorry. I didn't mean to say that. Trent say that "faggot" is just like a white man calling me a nigga . Anyway, man that shit fucked with me for a minute. Honestly, I still ain't over it. I come home from playing ball one day. Momma and pops still ain't got home from work yet. I knew Trent was home 'cause the front door was unlocked. But it wasn't no noise in the house. The TV was off, no music was playing. Our bedrooms are side by side and his door was shut. I just pushed it opened like I always do. Man, I opened that door and that big muscle bound nigga David was on his back fucking my brother!

I flipped! I mean I had no idea my brother was like that. I guess I should have seen it a little though. As much as we are alike, we are different. Trent in the orchestra with all the white people, he president of our class, in the choir, National Honor Society. Stuff like that. Niggas at our school just don't do that type of shit unless they real smart like Trent is. That's why I never really questioned it. He never asked me why the only thing I do is wanna play on the football and basketball team.

Anyway, I opened the door to see what he was doing, and that's what I saw. Man that nigga David is about three times bigger than me but I didn't care. I beat that nigga so bad I broke his nose. Blood was everywhere. And he about 24 or 25. Old ass fucking my little brother. And then Trent acting like a little bitch over in the corner crying telling me not to hurt him. I can't lie. When David ran out the house I turned on Trent and beat his ass too. It's the only time me and my brother ever fought since we was little. Shit you can't really say that was a fight. Trent don't even know how. He never had to.

All I could do was walk out. So much shit was going through my mind I felt like killing somebody. How could Trent do something like that? I just couldn't understand what kind of man would want to be with another man. What do they see in each other? And then I find out my brother, my twin brother, is one of them. Not my brother. My brother who I used to play cops and robbers with. Eat all the cereal from. Pull our little pee—pees out to see who had the biggest one. My brother who could have any girl at our school. They all loved his ass to death. Just couldn't be my brother.

I must have walked for about two hours trying to clear my head. I went back upstairs and to Trent's room. He was in there pulling the blood-covered sheets off his mattress. His face looked kinda swollen from when I hit him earlier. I knew we would have some questions to answer when our momma get home but I wasn't even thinking about that. All I was worried about was my twin brother. I didn't know what to say. I didn't understand.

"Trent I'm sorry for what I did. You mad?"

He didn't even look up.

"Trent why didn't you tell me you was like this?"

Still no response. I rubbed my hands over my cornrows, freshly done by a girl who wanna give Trent some pussy. I told her me and Trent look just alike, but she don't wanna give me none. Just Trent.

"Trent you gotta say something before I go crazy."

He looked into my eyes but still didn't say nothing. At least that was a start.

"You like that nigga David?" I really didn't give a fuck about him but I had to start the conversation somewhere.

More stares and no sound. I just sat down on the corner of the bed and let my head fall into my hands. I had run out of ice breakers. Then I heard my brother sniffle. Turning around and seeing my brother cry into his hands erased everything I had just seen. I realized my brother was in pain and the true battle wasn't in my acceptance. I just walked up to him and threw my arms around him. He started to cry right there on my shoulder. The last time I seen my brother cry was at our grandma's funeral, but everybody is supposed to cry then. This was his personal crisis. And I was willing to do whatever to help ease the hurt.

"Trent if you like what you were doing why you crying now?"

He wiped his face and sat down on the bed.

"Travis, you just don't understand."

"Well, make me understand."

Then he just started to talk. He told me how he has always felt different from everybody. How he never fit in with any crowd. How he cried his self to sleep almost every night before he stopped fighting it. How he wanted to kill himself after the first time because he felt so dirty. I just listened without interrupting him. I could tell he was relieved by finally sharing this with me. The more he talked the more I knew I had been ignoring all the signs that were there. I guess I just never wanted to think that my twin brother was like that.

"Your homeboy Charles is like that too ain't he?"

"Like what?"

"You know. A faggot."

That's when I got my first lesson in homo etiquette.

"Don't say faggot, Travis."

"So what do I call it?"

"It is not an it. We ain't talking about a disease. We talking about me"

"So you still ain't told me what to say."

My twin brother started to cry again. I got down on my knees in front of him and lifted his face, my face, to look me squarely in my eyes.

"I'm gay, Travis." His long hidden tears ran for freedom. He told me how he knew one day he was gonna have to tell me. He said he was scared of how I was gonna react and he felt like he was letting me down. This nigga made a 1190 on the SAT. I ain't even taken it yet. Trent knows what college he wanna go to. I'm scared I ain't gonna pass English which means you don't graduate.

He already knows where wants to live and work when he graduates. All I know is that I want Nia Long to be my wife. And he was scared I would let him down.

I had one more question.

"Trent, you sure you like dick instead of pussy? I mean I know you used to say you ain't no virgin, but have you really ever had some pussy to compare it to?"

He smiled then started to laugh. He laughed so hard some of the snot in his nose shot out on my shirt. I started to laugh too.

"Yes I'm sure."

And we spent the rest of the night talking, me asking questions I figured my brother had all the answers to. But he didn't. He didn't know why him. He said nobody ever touched him or anything like that when we were little. I can't lie and say that I understand now. I just know that I love my brother and always will. No matter what. Shit, we come from the same egg. Coulda been me? Well I don't know 'bout that but I guess it coulda been.

So now every dude I see with my brother I'm wondering. I mean I just assumed he was gonna be kicking it with other little nice, smart gay boys. But that nigga only kick it with straight up thugs! Everybody know about all the stories about niggas locked up doing shit. That's just 'cause they can't get nothing else. But niggas that free?

One night me and Trent were out back playing ball. We started talking 'bout our first time and he said he had been with more dudes than I been with girls. I couldn't believe that so he ran in the house to get a piece of paper and pen. He made two columns with my name on top of one side and his name on the other. We started listing everybody we had been with. Turns out I had fucked more but some of the names on his list blew my mind. I mean some of these dudes are on the football and basketball team with me. We done fucked some of the same girls together. And Big Pete that I buy my weed from. My brother said he and Big Pete get up all the time. You know one day Big Pete said something to me that I didn't pay any attention to but now it makes sense. I pulled up to buy a bag and he said why didn't I page him last night when he told me to. I was like, "what?" then he just looked at me all hard and started talking 'bout something else. He must have realized that I was me and not my brother. Ain't that some shit. Now I'm mad at my brother for not hooking up the free weed from his boy. Seems like I should have been cut a deal or something.

After we made the list I asked my brother if he was safe every time he had sex 'cause I was thinking about AIDS and all that. He flipped on me though. He said he has safe sex every time. I'm the one that don't like using rubbers. And he was right. But ever since that day I use one every time now. I guess before I thought AIDS was just some faggot shit and I couldn't get it. Sorry. I gotta get used to saying gay. I took a lighter out of my pocket and set the list on fire.

"Why you burn it? You don't want none of those girls to ever find the evidence?" I remember Trent joking.

"No, that ain't why. Just so we both know nobody on the list will ever come between us. No matter what column they in."

So now I know my brother is gay. (See, I'm getting better.) I told him I think he should tell our momma and pop. Momma cool. You know they say mommas know everything anyway. She probably already know. And pop don't say too much of nothing anyway. But Trent don't think he is ready for all that yet. But that's cool. Long as he know I still got his back. Who would have thought such a major difference would have bought us so much closer together? Ain't really no difference though when I think about it. Well, I still have to stop Trent sometimes when he get a little too X-rated for my ears. His social life the same as mine. He just can't walk through the mall holding hands with who he kick it with. I don't know. Trent might just try some shit like that. But that's my brother, my twin brother, and I still love him and ain't nobody gonna fuck with him 'cause he gay.

I just wish he would hurry his little faggot ass up so I can go smoke before momma and pops get home. ♣

LIVED IN

Justin Tranter

There's a woman I know. I know her so well. We slept in the same house for 18 years, 18 years, and three months. I slept inside her for nine. I breathed her breath, I ate her food, drank her water, I bathed in her blood. We slept in the same house for 18 years, 18 years and three months. We've been best friends ever since I let go of the baby sitter's leg, and I am pretty sure she knows everything about me, where I have been, who I've been. My friends and my ex-friends. My boyfriends and ex-girlfriends. When I have been nice and sweet. When I did something stupid in a stupid boy's sheets.

She has a face like you see in the magazines, and a body—and a body you don't. Her body is real; her body has lived through a life. Her body has seen four babies break through. Her body has seen a sister open a wrist, a sister twist the cap off of too many pills. Her body has felt the struggle of being a girl in a boy's swimming pool. Her body has felt the struggle of a misinterpreted bible telling her what to do. Her thighs have watched a son walk away, a son have a kid too soon, a son realize he was gay. Her body has had a date with divorce. Her body had a date with rape. Her body has taken quite the course.

I guess the editor of that magazine would call her fat. I would like that editor to know that I have seen my mom cry while looking in the mirror. I have seen my mom cry while standing on a scale. I have seen small children call her a whale. So, Dear Editor, my mom is not fat, she is strong, she is hard, she keeps a promise, she would kill for her children, she would die for my dad. She would fight a battle for the underdog, knowing she wouldn't win. So, Dear Editor, my mom's body is not fat, my mom's body is LIVED IN. ♣

THE DAY CHOOSES ME

Nadine Gartner

"Naaaaaaaaaaaadine!" The screech of my mother's voice jars me from my restful position on the couch. I reluctantly get up and make my way upstairs to her bedroom. Evidence of her imminent month-long trip to Israel lies everywhere. The ironing board and iron stand patiently in the family room, waiting to steam the pile of shirts that have accumulated on the floor. The vacuum cleaner rests against the stairs, serving as a reminder to my mother to clean the house before leaving. As I walk past the kitchen, the warm smells of my favorite dishes, baked chicken and broccoli soup, fill my nostrils. I laugh to myself as I realize that my mom embodies the perfect Jewish mother, as she ensures that I will eat well and stay comfortable during her absence.

When I reach her bedroom door, I don't dare to step over the threshold. Tank tops, bathing suits, shorts, Capri pants, and at least a dozen pairs of shoes are strewn about the room. Several large suitcases occupy the bed, just waiting to be filled with the various items that adorn the floor. My mom pops her head out from behind the bathroom door, where she is meticulously packing her toiletries into various compartments of her travel bag. Her wavy, brown hair awkwardly sticks out around her ears, telling me that she has been stressfully tugging at her scalp. The dark circles under her eyes underscore her frazzled state, and she wastes no time in getting down to business.

"What time do you want to go to the supermarket? I have a lot to do today. I have to finish cooking, vacuum the whole house, get this room in order—"

I cut her off before the myriad of chores stresses her out even more. "It doesn't matter to me, Mom. Whatever works best for you."

"Get the car ready. I'll be downstairs in a minute."

I linger at the doorway just long enough to notice her frantically smoothing down her hair and trying to look presentable for our trip to the store. As I head downstairs, I hear my mom complain to herself about the number of tasks she must complete before her flight tomorrow morning.

I choose this day to tell her I am gay.

On the way to the grocery store, my mother takes control of the wheel because my driving frightens her. As she carefully maneuvers the car through the winding streets of our suburban town, I tell her a funny story about one of my gay friends. I expect her to laugh and to appreciate my tale for its humor, but she instead seizes this opportunity to corner me with jarring questions.

"And what are *you*?" my mother asks me.

I freeze, knowing full well what she asks me, but not wanting to divulge my closeted self just yet.

"What do you mean, 'what am I'?" I awkwardly stammer, in a feeble attempt to buy more time to decide how to respond.

"Are you gay? The parents are always the last to know."

I stare straight ahead. Despite my earlier resolve, I now desperately wish that my mom would stop the car so that I could get out and run. Run far, far away to a place where I could be myself without having to worry about disappointing my loved ones. I grip the handle on the door and throw my body as far away from my mother as possible, but the station wagon restricts my movement to only a few inches. She has me trapped, and there is nowhere that I can turn.

It would be so easy for me to lie, my nine-year-old mind reasons. Mommy is at work all afternoon, so she'll never know if I go over to Lauren's house to play. When my mother comes home early and finds me absent, she calls Lauren's mom. I'm sent home, and as I cross the street that separates our houses, I decide to tell my mom that I was only returning Lauren's Barbie doll.

My mother doesn't believe me for a second. She slaps me across the face, the first time she has ever struck me, and yells at me for lying to her. Her shouts fill the entire house, and I feel my small body trembling.

"Never lie to me!" she screams. "Don't you ever lie to me! Do whatever else you want to do to me—yell at me, call me names, hit me! But, don't ever lie to me!" Her shouts eventually transform into hysterical sobs, but it will take months to rebuild a sense of trust. I vow to myself that I will never lie to her.

"I'M NOT STRAIGHT, MOM!" I shout the words, as if saying them louder will make them less painful to emit. "Is that what you want to hear?"

A stunned silence fills the car. I finally turn to look at my mother, as I have been staring straight ahead throughout my declaration, and I see her face quickly flush into a light shade of pink. She quietly answers, "Yes, if that's the truth. Don't you feel better now?"

Feel better? I feel as if the world has just stopped, but I am still spinning. I feel as if I have left my body to watch myself on a movie screen. I feel as if this is not really happening, and I literally pinch myself to prove that it is not a dream. But better? I wouldn't say that.

"I feel scared. I feel really scared."

"What? Why are you scared?"

I am afraid of how she will react, and that is why I let my mom continue to babble on. She just spoke to her friend, Bernice, again, and she wants to remind me for the third time that I ought to start thinking about my marriage plans.

"Bernice called this morning, and she wants me to tell you that you really ought to meet your mate in college. These are the best years of your life, and it only gets harder to meet people when you leave. Her son just got married at age thirty-eight—imagine that!—because he never met anyone in college."

"Thanks for the advice, Mom. I'll add 'Search for a Husband' to my list of priorities when I return to Bryn Mawr," I respond dryly.

"Don't laugh, Nadine. Bernice is a very smart woman, and I agree with her. Can't you meet more men at Bryn Mawr? It's extremely difficult to meet someone once you leave school and enter the real world."

I don't have the courage to come out to her just yet, so I decide to test her first: "Well, it's a damn shame I'm not gay, Mom."

My curt statement evokes my mom's limited knowledge of Yiddish: "Oh, gauvult. God forbid."

This is why I remain silent, I think to myself at the supermarket, as my mother and I make our way through the produce aisle. In between picking the choicest bananas and best-looking apples, she asks me the expected questions. "When did you start feeling this way? Was it Bryn Mawr? Have you spoken about this with your straight friends, or only other lesbians?" I answer in hushed tones, while simultaneously keeping an eye out for old high school classmates or teachers. Although I feel comfortable coming out to new acquaintances, I am not ready to surprise those who voted me "Most Likely to Succeed."

Somewhere in between picking the best head of lettuce and grabbing the freshest bag of baby carrots, my mother throws me for a loop. "I had a feeling," she says. "I thought that you and Ruth were involved back in high school."

I throw my head back in laughter, remembering how close Ruth and I were during our sophomore and junior years. Ruth is one of the straightest women I know.

I definitely had a huge crush on Ruth, though, I reminisce, as the Rabbi speaks about the original Ruth, the woman written about in the Torah. I subconsciously block out his voice and think instead of my Ruth, my best friend from camp, and the way that she makes me laugh and feel good about myself. I slowly drift back into consciousness after peering around the table and seeing the ten other adults, including my mother, intensely examine the Book of Ruth. I agreed to accompany my mom to this bible study because it is a way to celebrate Shavuout, one of the four major Jewish festivals, but I do not feel comfortable. All of the students are over the age of fifty, and they are much more interested in studying the ancient texts than I will ever be.

Suddenly, my ears prick up when one of the women questions Ruth's devotion to Naomi, saying that it seems to imply a romantic type of love. Relieved that I can finally contribute something to the discussion, I break in before the Rabbi has a chance to respond.

"Actually, that's exactly how a lot of feminists and queer theorists interpret the story. It's commonly used in Jewish lesbian commitment ceremonies."

My stunned mother stares at me with her jaw dropped, completely aghast as to where I attained such information and where I got the chutzpah to say it. The Rabbi appears just as shocked, but he recovers quickly to return to the notion of faith in the story. I put my head down and smile, congratulating myself for taking one more step outside the closet.

My mother momentarily pauses in her interrogation of my sexuality as we move through the cereal and snacks aisles. I am relieved that she has not yet run screaming from the supermarket. I begin to feel better about finally divulging my secret, but I am still waiting for some dreadfully negative repercussion for doing so. I have heard such horrific coming out stories, everything from getting kicked out of the house to being completely disowned by one's parents, that I am prepared to face the worst. I do not expect my mother to immediately accept or understand me. She has never known any lesbians, and who knows what stereotypes she harbors about us. Us, I think, feeling how coming out to my mom has strengthened my identification with the lesbian community.

As I reach up to the top shelf to grab a box of Special K cereal, I feel a hand upon my shoulder. I turn around and come face to face with my mother, the first time that we have locked eyes since my big announcement.

"I am so proud of you," she says. "You know, I am so proud of you."

My beaming mother wraps her arms around me and squeezes me with all of her strength. "You are so smart and such a go-getter. You will go far in this world."

"Thanks, Mom," I reply, appreciating her warm hug more than the words. The words I've heard before; hugs I don't receive as often because I am rarely home. I spend the school months in Bryn Mawr, Pennsylvania, and summers in Washington, D.C., working for various political organizations. This summer, I'm interning on the presidential campaign with the Democratic National Committee, and my parents are so excited that I earned the position.

"*I told everyone in Israel about it. I bragged to Grandma, Grandpa, Aunt Ariella, Uncle Danny, Rocha, and Edna. They are so impressed to hear that you are working for James Carville.*"

"*But, Mom, I'm not working for James Carville. I'm doing research for the Democratic Party, which is what he does, but I am in no way affiliated with him.*"

"*What does that matter? You think that the Israelis are going to understand what it means to do research for the Democrats? They know James Carville, so that is what I tell them.*"

It's futile to argue with her. Once she makes up her mind on an issue, there is no turning back. I am happy that she is proud of me, but I wish that she were proud of the true me.

As I wheel the cart of groceries through the parking lot and towards our station wagon, my mom places her hand on my back and gently rubs it. I feel as if I am a little girl again, back in the days when she could cure all ills with a glass of milk and some cookies. I long to return to that time, to crawl up in my mother's arms and to rest my head upon her breast. I want her to stroke my hair and to assure me that everything is okay. But I resist. Everything may not be okay this time, and I must give her whatever space she needs to deal with my news. I must be the strong one now, the one who can hold her hand and assure her that my life as a queer woman can and will go on.

We finish placing the grocery bags in the trunk of the car, and I move to return the shopping cart. Putting her hands on my arms, my mom stops me to give me a long, tight embrace. "I love you," she whispers, and, for the first time in my life, her pride in me seems real. Perhaps because I have finally been honest with her, I have given her a true daughter to be proud of. "As long as you are healthy and happy, I am happy for you." My eyes well up with tears, and I hug her even tighter. I don't ever want this moment to end.

This is the day I choose to tell my mother I am gay. The day chooses me. ♣

MY FRIEND, MY FAMILY,

TERRENCE

Walter Moyer

I transitioned from female to male many years ago. A friend from a church that I once worked for remembered that, and when she met Terrence she called me.

She was a contact person in the Philadelphia school system for gay and lesbian students and that's where she met Terrence. I am now legally male, I run my own accounting firm, and I've been in my neighborhood for 16 years. So, I guess, I was a good person to ask about transgender issues.

Terrence has learning differences and is developmentally delayed. We first had lunch before his high school graduation at the age of 21. He had lived too many years in foster care and lacked services that he should have been eligible for. He has always known he was male. After his graduation his foster home placement was discontinued. He then went into another home environment that was not suitable for him.

During this time Terrence and I spent a lot of time together, partly for mentoring and partly just two guys hanging out together. In 2001, Terrence's placement again was discontinued and all as he wanted to do was live with Uncle Wally.

So now Terrence lives with me and we are two bachelors hanging out. Terrence is working on his reading skills and volunteers three times a week with the elders. He is involved with the neighborhood and his church. Last December he started hormonal treatments in the process of transitioning from female to male. And he helped me write this story. His story. Our story about finding family. ♣

MOLLY: A One-Woman Play

Christa Kreimendahl

[*Lights up revealing a typical patient's room in a nursing home. A woman who appears to be in her late thirties enters. She walks with a slight limp. She faces the audience while speaking*]

Hi Miss Kathy, it's just me, Molly. Nice to see you all bright-eyed and bushy-tailed this morning. Well, as bushy tailed as can be expected from someone in your condition. Always bright eyed though, they can't take that from you, can they? You know I've been thinking a lot about you lately. I think you're different from the others, there's this something in your eyes. This hint of compassion. I bet you were full of good advice, that is when you could remember how to put a sentence together, or even just how to sound out a word. Yeah, I imagine lots of troubled souls dirtying your welcome mat and spilling their sins all over you. Don't worry about your family. I think sometimes families don't come to visit because it's hard for them. I think people who don't get visitors are more loved then the others. 'Cause it would be the hardest to see someone they truly love in your condition. It's kinda funny, I don't usually question the lives of my patients. That's why you must be different. I just come here to work, and to help people. To give back. Not to get involved.

For the last couple of weeks I've been asking myself, "What would Miss Kathy say?" Then I started to wonder, what would you want her to say? But then, I thought to myself, Molly, you've never wanted to share this with anyone before, and you shouldn't wonder what would she say if she could talk, you should take Miss Kathy as she is. God gave you Miss Kathy at this time in her life, a time when she can't give you advice. Maybe she's just suppose to listen. I know that you and me are virtual strangers and that it's awkward to have an intimate experience with a stranger. Believe me I know. Just the other day I was at my night job. I'm in the mens' room cleaning one of the toilets. That's my job. When this stranger, this whack job of a security officer comes in. I've seen him around. He's got this Buzz Aldrin haircut, and a great jolly belly that just screams at you. You know the type. So he walks in and sees me. Now I got my back to him so I don't see nothing, but I hear him. I know someone's there. Most men who come in while I'm cleaning either leave and go to another restroom or ask me to leave. This one's not going anywhere. So I figure I'll leave, but I want to finish wiping down the rim before I do. Just as all of this is running through my mind I hear ZIP. The guy starts doing his business in one of the urinals, right there. It's all soaking in when the guy says, "You know they have unisex bathrooms in Europe."

I'm a little concerned at this point, but I say "Oh yeah?"

"Yeah," he says. "In Switzerland or France."

I'm all done in the bathroom, but water boy's still going at it. I walk out just in time to see him shaking it off. Is that sexual harassment? Anyway, I end up having to flush the urinal behind him. On top of that he didn't even wash his hands. Washing your hands is a sign of education. My sister told me that. Polly, that was her name, my sister. I say "was" because she passed on a few years back. We were twins. Siamese twins. Weird huh? Yeah, most people think so. If this is too much for you just get up and jump around! Just kidding. I have a thing about overstepping someone's personal boundaries. I know a lot about that. When you share a hip with someone, boundaries don't exist.

Me and Polly didn't just share flesh and organs, we shared everything. Molly and Polly. God, I haven't heard those two names together in awhile. I hated it. Never just Molly or just Polly. Birthdays were the worst. Sweet sixteen, a big one, rights of passage and all that. Polly gets this beautiful diary leather bound, the whole nine. It had this tiny key with a satin ribbon attached to it. Me? Well I get a new nightgown it was really pretty. Pink satin, with this intricate lacing along the bottom, cuffs, and some around the collar. But, of course, this nightgown was made for two. The way I see it Polly made out with a private diary and a new nightgown. That doesn't seem fair does it?

Years later, this nightgown was still around. A little worn, some of the holes that clothes get when they've been washed a lot. Kind of like me.

[Pause]

So it's time for bed and I'm helping Polly into the nightgown. She was always weak, from the time she was born. I'm pushing her little hand through the arm when she looks at me with that face, the helpless one. Polly was good at being helpless. So she looks at me and says "Do you ever wish Mom and Dad had separated us?" We both know that would've meant her death. "Of course not," I told her. And just for that moment, that split second, I meant it. I really did. As I'm helping her get under the covers she looks at me, same face, and says "I love you." "I love you too." I said, and I meant that too. That night I slept like a log, as usual. And Polly had scrunched down under the covers. She always did that, scrunched down in this way that gave me a stiff neck in the morning.

[Pause.]

This time, the nightgown had gathered around her mouth and nose, and in her struggle had pulled tight to her face.

People ask me all the time if I feel like I'm missing something. See people got this idea, maybe from TV, I don't know, but they think that all twins have some sort of magical connection. Like reading each other's minds or something stupid like that. Not me and Polly, we didn't have that, nothing like it. Missing something? No. More like finally, finally having something. Normalness. Is that a word? I'm getting away from myself. I've never done this before, told someone.

[Pause.]

Even though I slept like a log, I woke up startled, a little out of breath, and Polly was struggling. That's when I saw her, with her weak, useless hand trying to free herself. At that moment I had a choice, and I chose to be normal. What's wrong with that? I had to carry Polly to the phone to call the ambulance. I knew she wouldn't make it, but being connected as we were there were complications to consider. Carrying her to the phone I felt her weight. And in a moment of pure clarity I saw her, I finally saw her for what she'd been all these years. Weight, tugging and pulling on me. I looked right at her, and I said "I hate you" and I really meant it.

Wow. [Silence.]

You know Miss Kathy, maybe having a terrible memory is really a blessing in disguise. Well I don't know, I bet you don't have anything you wish to forget. Not you. Not with those eyes. [Pause.]

Thank you Miss Kathy, for being such a good listener. I'm gonna make sure you're taken care of. Don't you worry about a thing. ♣

A PREGNANT SKY

Arielle Davis

I often have personal revelations while driving in the car, oddly enough. I guess my mind is just a little blanker when I'm on the road. One particular day I was driving southbound on I-75 toward my home in Gainesville. The sky was just fabulous. It was a hurricane sky. Not a storm, but the big belts of clouds that encircle and cross the sky like huge arms. They are the feeders of a hurricane and they always excite me in a way; the way animals get excited when a storm approaches.

As I drove, glancing now and then at the wondrous formations above me, it occurred to me that I'd seen these same shapes somewhere before on my own body. I had just given birth to my daughter no more than six months before and the experience had left me with some pretty bad stretch marks all over my belly and legs. But at that moment, I realized that they looked just like these glorious feeder arms of the hurricane. I decided to claim this hurricane as a part of my own personal pregnancy and birthing story. My daughter's birth was the hurricane and these marks on my body, were and always will be, the beautiful creation left behind by her birth, just like the feeder arm clouds were the remnants of that storm. Sure, I still get self-conscious sometimes of my appearance. But I now have a powerful, positive image to counter the negative emotions that I occasionally feel toward my body.

Now when I start to think negatively about my body image, I remind myself instead that I have been tattooed with all the fantastic, goddess-like strength, power, and fury of a hurricane. Embracing this positive body image has allowed new perceptions to blossom. My rounded, jiggly tummy is a mark of my motherhood. When I see the bulge that used to be tight and flat, it reminds me that it looks like that because my baby used to live there. The stretch marks that have recently started to show on my breasts are an emblem of my nurturing and love for my child. Had I stopped breast-feeding at six months, perhaps they would have never shown. These scars chronicle my life as well as my daughter's entrance into the world and I wear them with pride. ♣

Section Four

[VIOLENCE, ABUSE, SURVIVAL]

THE BODY

Sherisse Alvarez

some days she will forget she has a body
some days she will want to invent a new one
one that is smaller invisible will be coerced into fashionable
    clothing
escape the men staring and asking for favors
one that is bigger to ward off their loud mouths

one that is decorated with beads tela and colors
from her motherland one that is suited to
wear leather bands around the wrists and chains around the waist
the place that will not be held down one that is free to move

like a father's cough one that is never ill or slowed down
by the sadness lingering on street corners one that knows
how to satisfy itself use its own hands and fingers for good pleasure
some days she will have to be reminded how to laugh
how to hear herself laughing loudly
and for a long while over and over again
some days she will think she is on the wrong side of the sea
some days she will need to walk outside without saying a word
just to know that she can
to breathe in slowly the still air
listen to herself breathe until she knows it by heart
like song
like the memory that is still fresh that still stings like a truth

the first breaking bone
the first vicious pinch from her mother's fingers
the first ugly word a man whispered into her ear
the words she spoke back or didn't
the kiss that ached in the belly for days
the first splinter someone carefully removed for her

some days the girl will need to make noise like the kind that
follows lightning
the kind that follows death
silence
some days she will come back to the scents

that remind her of first love ripe skin that stood still for her
the same smell returning years later when she is with a woman
and knows she may never love a man in quite this way
the almond and lilac and lavender oils they will initiate each
    other with
the moans and chants
her breasts and ass
erect nipples and the things they forget to say
the things they choose to say later
the things they reveal when the other is sleeping
the things that they notice
wide open sun draping over the curve of a spine
the way their hands cross and toes dance
the ways they have loved
the way the tears fall
the way everything becomes wet
she will apologize for the mess
some days the girl will not feel her body
will feel out of her skin
some days all the girl will do is write about what she witnesses
what she thinks she knows
she will come back to the body of her work
the secrets shattering like a word ♣

LAST DANCE

Mikhail Lewis

We were at the school dance. The song was girls ask boys. I stood next to you on our side. I wanted, wanted, wanted to kiss you. Just looking at you gave me ideas and the beginnings of an action would form in my head. I'd find, in my mind, my lips, already moving, my arms stretching, my fingers groping. It was dark. The dark and the lights, your posture, the entire mood.

I was standing against the railing on the wall, my back to it, tapping my hands lightly, looking at you. There were spots of colored lights in your eyes and in your hair. Your clothes where muted dark colors in the light.

No one asked either of us to dance. We just stood there, together. You didn't look at me. They played that fucking No Doubt song a third time. You sat down. You were watching the dancers. Most of the kids where standing in big clumps, the boys and the girls, except for the antisocial kids. They sat together, sort of, in the bleachers. I could see a girl with short blue-dyed hair positioned' face up on one the seats. It looked as though she'd cut her hair by herself.

I sat down next to you. I felt strange, over near the wall, away from everyone else, next to you. These girls started pointing at us and I stood up. I looked at you and you finally looked up at me. I looked away.

You stood up. The chair was between us. We looked at each other. The song ended and the Cardigan's song from *Romeo &*

Juliet started playing. All these girls went to dance with each other. The boys all tried to avoid. I blinked and almost looked away. I smiled instead. You didn't smile back.

You pushed aside the chair and then stopped. I thought about dancing, in the middle of the dance floor, with someone. I stopped smiling and stepped forward. You took your hands out of your pockets. You opened your mouth to say something. I licked my lips. My hands felt sweaty. I said, "You want to go outside?"

Two guys walked up. You looked at them and then back at me. Your fist smashed into the side of my jaw and I fell over a chair. I stood up, my ears ringing, you mouthing the word "faggot." A chaperon came over and asked if there was a problem. I picked up the chair and walked off. It was so important not to rub my chin. I don't know why.

I went outside and rested my head on my knees, facing the door. The door opened and I turned my head to stare at the ground. Some people walked by. "The music was crap," someone said. When I looked up I saw the girl with blue hair and her friends turn the corner.

I went back inside the door. I started to walk back into the room, the girls pointing more now, when the Principal stopped me, "Once you're out you're out."

I looked in at the dance; "Oh yeah, I forgot."

He said, "Sure."

I went outside looking back at the closed door. I felt like crying. I was taking big gulps of air. I clenched my hands until the nails dug in and locked my jaw until it sent sharp pains up my face. I walked home. I couldn't see the streetlights clearly. When I got to my door I dropped my keys. I bent down to get them and instead beat my head into the cement step. I gasped again and picked them up.

I lay in bed until the pain made me sleep. ♣

GAY BASHED

Rachel Kasa

Youth holds the fingertips of reality lightly
I lay my hand out on the ground
and the flesh runs off like water,
Blackly, the taut skin seeps into the soil
obscene whiteness of bone
I lick my lips to feel the salt & flesh of sweat,
and taste nothing but dry death

I'm sinking as I'm speaking
Prejudice was never a word I wanted to know,
Perhaps someone will dig me up
1,000 years from now/ and give me a name,
a name that doesn't start with FUCK YOU, you _____. ♣

FINAL MISTAKE *(lyrics)*

Alicia Champion

Take me in
Let me drown with them
For I have sinned
More than those you've damned
And what do we do
In the midst of so much hate

But sit and read the news
Of more unwanted pain

Seeing it time and again
Seeing it with no end
How long will it take
Before our own death is our final mistake
Let me be
The center on which all hate can be released

Through the pages of time
We've been the victims of our very crimes
With our anger stemmed from fear
Of all we want to deny
So many loves have I seen pass me by
And I'm such a young privileged soul
With so many gifts that fill our lives
We still give in and let go

To the weakness inside
The weakness that makes our love hide
How long will it take
Before our own death is our final mistake
Let me be
The center on which all hate can be released
We look down upon, hurt and curse the unknown
Brandon, Matt Shepherd
Those at Columbine know
In order to raise someone up
We bring somebody down
And laugh at them like we would at a clown
How long will it take
Before our own death is our final mistake
Let me be
The center on which all hate can be released ♣

ALL THE NEWS THAT'S

FIT TO PRINT

Rachel Kasa

Coma Falls Slowly
World Sickens
African Babies Die of AIDS Just Like Homos
Dateline: January 8, 2001
Even when we don't see the breathing suck and gasp
and stop.
Clock time twists and burns,
slow motion cauterization,
flopping eyeless as toxic fish.
There is no womb any longer
Just a hole and a cunt.
The stoic unresolved to make it better reigns,
No cautionary tales reside in the collective memory,
For memory itself has been un-persistent,
and the collective turned to an army of java
writers and garment factory workers,
United by the corporations they serve. ♣

THE BOYS OF

DOLORES PARK

Rachel Kasa

hiding from the flickers
it's too bright to see today
proudly bronzed-warriors-
mourning on parade.
long-limbed, short-lived.

How many die without trying
how many live without trying.
swaying their bodies to an invisible rhythm,
basking in the glitter
sucking the nectar dry
swimming inside the bulging silence
making conversation until the light falls away.
whose turn is it to fade,
and does it even frighten anymore.
the sadness slips outward anyway,
soon everyone will notice anything,
rippling in the late afternoon sun. ♣

POWELL STREET,

DECEMBER

TWENTY-SEVENTH

Ellen Freytag

In between Corpus Christi and BART
a shoddy saxophone on the corner
pulls gold teeth away from moist reed
mid-song to shout at her
that she could "almost pass for a boy,
just a few more of them fucking
hormone shots and"
She recalls
that Augustine pondered how one
could remember forgetfulness;
around her: two solid blocks
of one voice and eyes and eyes
mercifully blurring to the texture
of a Chinese pear. Four years earlier
a man had prepared her for these moments:
how to write poems, love Faulkner,
and play her favorite song
over and over, closer and closer to fine.

Of course Augustine was searching for God,
the saxophone for a quarter or
a greater sin to absolve him, but
was Mathew Shepherd Jesus Christ
or was Jesus Christ Mathew Shepherd?
Rhythm of her train:
Yoknapatawpha, Yoknapatawpha;
as the lights of the tunnel
passing her under the bay
shout green at steady increments,
She tries not to yearn for another sound,
one she has forgotten
though remembers hearing:
the fly crying behind her headboard
late at night as a child,
a fly crying behind a Great Wall. ♣

WHEN BLOOD WROTE

A POEM

Davey S.

The first time that blood wrote a poem,
there was no one,
nothing to staunch the flow.
It poured out onto the page,
washed notebooks crimson,
soaked through reams of pain,
a flood too heady for mere paper.
My pen tore through wet pages,
useless.
I pinched wounds closed in urgency to keep on living,
ink not worth the gaping wells.
Demanding they heal,
I willed them shut,
so tight that blood wrote nothing.
Now leafing through old lives
I find a papery scar:
the perfect vellum for my life's ink
leaking rusty from wells lovingly reopened,
just enough to scratch out words,
my name: a claim laid.
It says my body: mine ♣

LIKE ME

Davey S.

You could have been me—not that that's so great, but—
You could have been reading at three winning essay contests,
graduating early.
You could have been where I am now,
surely a finer place for a poor girl to have gotten.
But you do not make eye contact
owl-eyed scrawny slouch
telling how you got beat up, again.
A bruise, a broken pair of glasses
I try to comfort,
knowing that my murmuring means nothing,
words are crap, and fists are real.
I come crying sometimes, and you listen—
The rich girls don't like me:
poor country girl tomboy
genderfuck.
After all, I can't wear dresses,
I can't speak with effortless grammar and charm,
I can't throw a party,
even if my life depended on it.
So what use are Math, Psychology, Comp Lit, Sociology?
What use the skill to deconstruct my own hard won identity?
They teach me to take my world apart, spread it out,
examine every cutting shard: a race, a class, a sex, a gender.

This is Wisdom; this is Academia.
But whether whole and ignorant, or on the floor in pieces,
each point understood like (x, y),
I am still the poor kid, still muddy-kneed and lisping,
I still got beat up at the bus stop.
And this is about class, and this is about gender,
and I can speak the language of my oppressor.
But fancy words don't make them like my
flat chest, dirty mouth, frizzy hair, and muscled arm.
In their tongue, I quote Marx.
In their tongue, I study Weber.
But we know that's not me in the classroom;
I'm not her.
I'm the one who holds you after we both woke up sobbing from
dreams of po' white country boys with big fists and scrawny,
owl-eyed children. ♣

ROBBIE'S DIARY:

A SUICIDE IN POEMS

Robbie Kirkland

[*Robbie Kirkland's mother Leslie Sadasivan submitted these poems after the 14-year-old committed suicide. "Robbie was teased and harassed in school from a young age because he was perceived as gay. He was not happy to be gay and felt rejected by his Catholic Church, our homophobic society, and his classmates. Our family loved, supported, and accepted him but it was not enough," says his mom. He would be 20 today if he were still alive. Most of the poems were written between the ages of 12 and 14 and reflect his painful struggle.*]

ANYTHING GOES

Anything Anything
Anything goes
Wild and crazy, jellied toes
Dukes, kids, dogs, cats
Hit a bowling ball with ten baseball bats
Rambunctious and rowdy, yup that's me
Come on, come on, imagination is the key
Smile for yourself

Smile for me
Sing and shout slither and slide
I eat bacon totally deep-fried
Forget about all your woes, because anything
Anything, anything goes! (*Written July 1994, age 12, two years before his suicide*)

DEATH

Death is neither love nor hate, but a cruel demented twist of fate,
We lose those we love
And pray to God they go to heaven above
We hurt the ones we love the most
How can we wake up and eat our buttered toast
We mourn and cry,
But somehow, some way we will get by.
People kill
Blood will spill
We don't like to wait
But alas it is too late. (*Written July 1994 at age 12*)

I WISH YOU THE BEST

I hope you'll remember me
I will remember you
I wonder if you see that
I must leave
I just cannot stay
I did not want it that way
So, I will leave.
I will leave you behind, along with the rest of my life
I will miss you

Oh I will miss you but
Don't look back for now
I must pack for my journey
Good Bye
Good Bye
Please don't cry
I wish you the best. (*Written August 1994 at age 12*)

I'M DYING AND NO ONE CARES

I try to stand and walk
I fall to the hard cold ground.
It feels as if to life I'm no longer bound.
The others look and laugh at my plight.
Blood pours from my nose,
I am not a pretty sight.
I try to stand again but fall
To the others I call
But they don't care
The pain is unbearable
The world is not fair
I'm lost and cold
I wish someone would lend a hand to hold
My tears mix with my blood
The End of my life
It nears
I'm Dying and no one cares
The pain. The pain. THE PAIN!
I scream in pain!
My body shakes in violent spasms
I cry out in pain again!
I scream
My blood pours like a stream
I'm Dying and no one cares
I scream in pain one last time and then it's over.
I am Dead and no one cares. (*Written August, 1994 at age 12*)

FADE OUT

Kill yourself and kill me too
You know why I fell for you
You fall yourself past my basement
Your head hit the pavement
I hope it doesn't hurt
When they treat you like dirt
Cuz your eyes are open as they stare
But half of you just ain't there,
Never see me smile
I'll just fade out in the meanwhile
Fade out
fade out
fade out. (*Written October 1996, age 14*)

CHANGING

The river washes over me
washes away impurity
The sunshine from above
I can fly like a dove
I laugh and smile
You ought to stay for a while
The water turns to blood
My life is turned to mud
The sun goes down
I crash land far from town
I scream and cry
You ought to say good-bye. (*Written November 1996*)

LIE

Do you lie in the dark?
Is your ignorance your bulwark?
Why can't you see?
You're just like me
You don't get metaphors
You could open so many doors but they stay closed
I screamed when you posed
You move beyond your own ideas
I can destroy your poor lil' boy
Join my cult or you'll be a dolt
Just keep lying in the darkness
Sins you can't confess. (*Written November 1996, age 14, one month before his suicide*)

LOST

Lose myself in the rain
I can no longer feel the pain all is quiet before the rain
Rain pours down on me
I drown in the blood-filled sea
The heart was bleeding
What my life was needing all I have to go is one more mile
I really don't wanna smile
I think that I could kill but I don't know if I will
But I can't find myself in the rain but I suddenly feel the pain
Life is lost
Sold for a cost
falling down
leave this town
fall behind
leave it all behind
The rain stops.
The pain stops.
My heart stops. (*Written November 1996, age 14, one month before his suicide*) ♣

MYSTERY OF YOUR

BLUE (*lyrics*)

Alicia Champion

You sent me a picture of when it began
Your gentle expression shed marks by his hands
Such a tender soul of a child
Scarred by the sadness of a father's warring mind

Leaves you helpless
Leaves you alone
Who can you turn to
When daddy's right at home

And is this what he did to you not so long ago
Your eyes hold rivers behind a smile you don't know
If all your innocence was lost in your youth
Then tell me how you trap me like you do
In the Mystery of Your Blue
In the Mystery of Your Blue

Lost in a world you once called your home
Your only embraces feel as cold as stone
You blossom older while you're pulled at your roots
And eaten alive by the seed that is you

Leaves you bleeding
By your own hand and by his
What a lonesome feeling
That could bring you down to this

Chorus
With years gone by, that gaze still remains
The reluctant smiles that trace the shame
Now I behold your shining grace
And I see it
I can't believe it
For at your base is that very same
Five year old face

And he'll never touch you again as long as I'll know
These eyes need to cease their hold and let the
tears flow
If there was one thing I would ask of you
It's to take my hand
Let me see you through
The Mystery of Your Blue
The Mystery of Your Blue ♣

PRETTY

Amy Weaver

Someday I will be pretty
No longer the little fat girl in therapy,
Because I sat on my self-esteem and broke it.
Choked up 22 years of spoon-fed abuse and candy-coated rape
Drank down the years of secrets and sin,
Locked within a brittle frame
Behind dark curtains and closed doors
See, in the South, that's where we keep our secrets
And a little girl weeps the sound of Ole Southern hymnals
The coursing of pride through veins worn thin,
a body, a heart, a soul worn thin and . . .
Amazing grace never sang so beautifully,
She just never sang for me
Left me another casualty of low self-esteem
Chasing beauty that is only skin deep
Someday, maybe I will see,
That I am not trapped in this shell,
I've been blessed with it
And 10,000 sit-ups won' t make me whole,
Or beautiful—just a fool
Living up to someone else's expectations
Someone else's definition of who I ought to be
got me chasing each new "Diet of the Century"
Like I have something to lose

Before becoming more of a person
Someday, I will hunger for sweet dreams that still elude me
No longer drowning the nightmares in whiskey
And running away
From the mirror
From the scarred little girl
Staring back through haunted eyes,
Like she knows she'll never be enough
I want to show her that the dreamers
Are the only ones with vision
And you don't need to be thin to listen or pretty to see . . . .
Beauty wrapped in brilliance
Danger slow-dancing with decadence
A snake's deadly venom laced with a whore's knowing kiss
All of this hidden beneath layers of flesh
And it may be scarred, but they are
Battle scars
Marks of pride
Because I earned them
Known love and been forgotten
Traded innocence for violation
Trust for degradation and
Truth for isolation
But here I stand hoping someday
My inner beauty will be the first thing you see
Because there is more to me than will ever fit inside this body
And someday I'll look into the mirror and see a little girl smiling
Because she knows she's pretty. ♣

NIGHTCHILD (*lyrics*)

Alicia Champion

Why are you so far away
I wanna hold your hand a little longer
I want so badly to stay
Make what I have with you a little stronger
Now I'm afraid to let go
To what feels so safe
And you . . .
How can I prove that you . . .
Are my child in the night
When I see you alone in the rain
I wanna grab my sword and fight
I'll never know the spell you cast on me or how it's
let me be
Sitting here asking you to please just believe that
I could
Be everything you need and more
I'll slay any dragon if it's you I'm fighting for
Would you look at me just one more time and maybe
you will see
That I'll be your angel, yeah that's me

I hide so well the tears that streak my face
I know we're both growing older
And perhaps it isn't even my place
But hey, it was you who made me bolder
Now I know you can't wait for me
But just know that you're all my eyes can see my . . .

Child in the night
When I see you alone in the rain
I wanna grab my sword and fight
I'll never know the spell you cast on me or how it's
let me be
Sitting here asking you to please just believe that
I could
Be everything you need and more
I'll slay any dragon if it's you I'm fighting for
Would you look at me just one more time and maybe
you will see
That I'll be your angel, yeah that's me

So I don't know if I'm in love with you
Or if this is something I can explain
All I know is I wanna be near to you
And hold you and tell you it's okay
'Cause when I look into your eyes
I'm floored by what I see
Everything that I adore
And all I wanna be my . . .

Child in the night
When I see you alone in the rain
I wanna grab my sword and fight
I'll never know the spell you cast on me or how it's
let me be
Sitting here asking you to please just believe that
I could
Be everything you need and more
I'll slay any dragon if it's you I'm fighting for
Would you look at me just one more time and maybe
you will see
That I am your angel, yeah that's me ♣

Section Five

[LOVE, SEX, LOSS]

LAST LESSON

Ellen Freytag

The metronome ticks between us
from where it is muffled beneath
the covers of your bed.
My hands bloom bright blisters
into the otherwise silent room.
I walk miles to the station
to catch the train to your city,
gripping the cheap plastic handle
of a guitar case someone once gave
away. Mid-song, my fingers
are unable to shape the next chord.
You have become worse than
disappointed: indifferent—or maybe
you are anxious for this
to be over. But I still would not
undiscover the touch of your hand
these months for anything. Later, back
on the train, I watch the blistering
sun slipping, disappearing
beneath the bridge and into the bay.
I think of how we meet her
coming in as I am leaving,
each of us carrying her guitar.
My eyes still water. Your eyes are
still water. Her eyes still the waters. ♣

WAITING TO EXHALE

Mikhail Lewis

You lit the joint and drew in your breath, long and deep. You expected the smoke to diffuse around your hair, rolling up, but instead it shot at your eye, catching you in the act.

"Shit."

He giggles, "Shh, my mom will hear you."

You exhale and stifle a cough.

"You're just paranoid, man."

You pass it to him and he puts his lips to it, inhaling. His lips are pink and clear, darker than his skin, pale in the light. The whites of his eyes shine through the room. There is a small lamp in the corner with a pillowcase on it. You look back over and his eyes are closed. You hit his shoulder and smoke explodes out of his nose and mouth, his eyes opening.

"Shit man, your eyes are bloodshot."

He smiles. "Yah?"

He passes you back the joint and you flick the lighter. The spark comes up but it doesn't light. You do it again and it lights but you let go. He laughs, covering his mouth. You adjust your grip on it. You light it again and the instant you put it to the joint, already inhaling slowly, the smoke hit your eye and you drop them both. Your head falls back and you rub your eyes, tears dripping down.

"Shit," he says, grabbing the lighter and the joint, rubbing the spots they'd burnt. He licks his finger and rubs your jeans.

"You'll fuckin' set something on fire."

Embers had fallen on your lap and he is rubbing your thighs. He finally gives up and puts the joint and the lighter back in the box, under the incense. You have your eyes closed, imagining his eyes, his lips. Your hands lay at your sides, motionless, huge.

"What are you thinking?" he asks. You don't know how long it has been. You imagine his arms around you. He puts his arm around you and soon you're in his lap, both his arms around you from behind, both buzzing from the pot, and you from the feel of his hands on your chest. His mouth is near you. You swivel your head around and open your mouth.

"Nothing."

"Come on. You have to be thinking about something."

You asked him how long it had been, how long you'd been thinking.

"A couple of minutes?" he says. "Just tell me."

You start to say that you are thinking about how much you like him and how much you want to touch him, to fall asleep with him, to just feel his lips, with your fingers, opening them and closing them again, feeling how smooth they are, how they contrast with the skin around his mouth—

"I was thinking—"

His mother knocks on the door.

"What's going on in there?"

You smiled at him and he glares at you. "Nothing mom."

"I thought I heard something."

"Nothing, mom."

"You boys don't get too loud now."

"Okay."

You giggle and he throws up his hands. "See?" You laugh and he leans forward. Your head hits the ground suddenly and you keep going. He laughs.

"You just fell over."

You begin laughing hysterically, gasping and shaking. He leans over you, his arm coming out of the ground near your head. You stop laughing and just lay, panting, your mouth stretched out in a huge smile. He laughs and falls on you. You start laughing again, shaking under his weight. He hits his head against yours and swears, softly.

"Fuck. Shit that hurt."

You giggle, your eyes sliding over to the door and back. He looks in to your eyes and you imagine you both sitting together, passing smoke. He kisses you once on the lips and gets up smiling. You lay there for half a minute.

"You hungry?"

You shake your head. You don't want to eat. He turns on the television and the Nintendo. He gives you a controller. You take it and move over near the TV. He is playing and you start laughing again. He pauses the game and looks at you.

"What? What."

You smile back at him and laugh again, shaking your head. He starts playing again, laughing every time you do. You shake your head back and forth quickly every time. You fall back again and gave up the controller. You are still falling when you wake up. You lift your head up looking around. He sits on his bed with a book. He looks up and closes the book, marking his place. You get up and sit down on the corner of the bed.

"Dinner's ready soon." You nod slowly and stretch. "You spending the night?"

You yawn and try to nod yes.

"Cool," he says.

You look at each other and hear his mother's voice, "Dinner. Boys!" rising at the end of the sentence. He looks at you and laughs. He opens the door and you go out first. You eat dinner with his parents and head back upstairs. You eat twice as much as normal. His dad says things like, "Growing boys, blah, blah." You say, "Sir" and "Thank You" and "Please pass the butter." You rinse your plate in the sink and set it on the counter. He leaves his plate on the table and—as soon as the tip of your dish touches the counter—runs upstairs. You sit down in his room as he gets out his box. He fixes the joint and puts it to his mouth. He holds it out to you and positions the lighter for you. You tilt your head back so the smoke won't hit your eyes, and you inhale. You hold it until that mist you see in the dark appears in the light and then cough it out. You cover your mouth with your cold hands and stifle the cough. He looks at you with his head turned, holding in his own smoke. You look back, waiting for the joint. He leans over and puts his mouth over yours. You inhale. ♣

CHERIE

Lauren Eve

It shouldn't matter; it should just happen one way or the other. No borders, no lines, no labels—that is my dream. No boxes or shelves or closets. No out or in. No coming or going or confusion. This is how it should be. No anger or fear, no more than the next person. No numbers or statistics shouted out anymore.

When I met her, she was still wild; I'd yet to tame her. I was tame and she would change that too. We just started talking one day, was it May? Maybe, perhaps a little earlier. We met in the Ani DiFranco chatroom and for one reason or another just kept talking. We had very little in common, even less then than we do today. It is impossible to know what color it was, but I know it wasn't black anymore.

The fairies buzzed around and gave us friendship. If it is the sunshine that grows the blooming flowers in spring, that gives strength to the weak and questioning, if the sun does all that, then it is the sun that was strongest that year. We met when we were both young, kids really. She had just been arrested for being drunk, loud, and naked downtown. I didn't know what to believe so I believed it all and still I didn't believe a word.

We were fast friends, having nothing in common, except maybe some music, movies, books. We both loved Ani DiFranco, Sleater-Kinney, *Annie On My Mind*, *All Over Me*. We discussed fairies and dreams. We drew each other into the other's world with names and characters and events. We were so honest sometimes it was scary and, as we got closer, the honesty dug deeper.

We became perfect typists. I learned how to scan my photographs into my computer so she could see the girl she was talking to. We shared gossip of people we had never met and complained about schools we had never seen. We drifted in and out of each other's lives, connected only by modern technology of gray wires and tall, tall phone lines.

An email, a little message, an hour a day—it all became important. It was not most important; we did not abandon the lives we still had to perform daily. Not always getting a stranding ovation, we turned to each other occasionally for the support we had lacked on stage. Our fears became skin-deep and accepted. We treaded upon ideas until they were each other's and ours and pondered.

She moved after two years of us still having not met. The future was daunting and scary; we rarely mentioned it yet planned it furiously.

"Next year," I'd say.

"When you are in college," she'd start.

Boys came and went. Crushes, giggles, sex, hook-ups, small dicks, large cocks. Then a girl. Then two. Then a boy again. We grew jealous of the other's partner, our bond thickened. It was hazy pinks and lazy blues. It was deeper than explainable. Information and magic spilled upon us. We knew not what to do about it but took it and stored it and loved it.

Perhaps we had never been the normal children that had been longed for. Perhaps the goddesses smiled harder on the days we were born. The antique yearnings of humans had become ours for keeps. We were horrible and wonderful all at once. Grade point averages higher than "normal," jobs, respect, friends.

I drank in school. She drank at parties. She rolled on E; I was stopped and searched by the police. I stripped at parties; she danced naked in the streets in the summer rain. We both sliced, wished to die, fell in love, saved each other. We failed to do anything for ourselves, instead quenched the other's desire for normality and certainty and love.

Together we lived under the full moon and over the rainbow. We rode skateboards, metros, shotgun. Hoodies, short skirts, wide pants, tank tops, wife beaters, my brother used to beat me, fuck-me boots, fuck me! Fuck me! I'd rather make love to you, I love you, I want to hold you, shush shush shush.

Our hair was pink, blue, red. We were high, drunk, sober, drugged, rolling, smoking, sleeping, snorting, clean. She took two classes a day, worked herself harder than the businessmen in their suits, had new dreams as the moon changed. I took seven classes, wrote her stories as requested; it was my love in life— besides her, of course.

We grew older, stronger, weaker apart, in love, love, love. We talked on the phone every few months, when the fears came, when the loneliness took over and life was ugly again. Money, grades, parents, friends; it all flew out the window. Like the birds and the bees. Like the fairies. On coke, heroin, 'shrooms, pot, vodka, gin, beer. Underage, underloved. We were clichés and above it all and flying with wings spread so far it was easy to lose control and easy to soar and easy to nose-dive. Love, cum, love, sex, fuck, sweat, burning, sickness. Sick. Queer. Dyke. We grew closer, together, in love. We grew into one.

I believe her now; she was arrested for being drunk, loud, naked downtown. She is smooth and salty and sexy and safe in my arms. My bed. My life. We were fast friends and slow lovers. Good little girls and wild kids. Sluts, dykes, geeks, punks, skaters, writers, ravers, stupid, brilliant, waitresses, cops, students, teachers, slicers, suiciders, smokers, drinkers, addicts, saviors.

Together.
Everyday we wake up.
She says.
I am not your brother.
I say.
You are a naked dork.
She says.
You made me naked.
I say.
I love you.
She says.
Shush.
Everyone who ever said that to her has left her.
I say.
I will never leave you.
I will hold her tightly.
We soar together.
Together.
Together.
It is beautiful ♣

PARKS AND PICNICS, CLASSROOMS AND BATHROOMS

Rachel Kasa

There should have been a beginning.
Her eyes always shone like candles,
even when she slid right past me.

Swans drifting to the other shore.

Even when I couldn't talk, I knew
there was a swell that pitched me up beyond the others,
and a scent that wouldn't go away.

Last year, I thought it was the weather.
But lately, there have been no explanations except my own.
Even then it couldn't have been a sin,
since living "correctly" always seemed so wrong.
I was never one to admit I felt things.

Or tell the world all about the fist in my
stomach,
that sucked breath that always came,
when she passed,
and he never
did. ♣

BOY

James Patrick Gillece III

Boy stared intensely at his computer screen, his usual activity late at night. He had just clicked a link claiming it would send him to "Hot Gay Anal Action," an offer he could not turn down. As he did so an ad popped up. Boy waited for the small hourglass to disappear from the screen as the pop up ad loaded. The first thing that came up on the screen was a face, a sharp face with a goatee. Boy found himself staring at this picture, this personal muse. It didn't occur to him that thousands of people were looking at the same picture at that very moment. He felt as if he was the only one and that this man, this beautiful man was staring out only at him, and then he knew that they had a connection. Boy printed out the picture and folded in up, but he still remained in a trance.

"Still up?" Boy's mother had entered the room, "What are you doing on the computer this late at night?"

"Oh!" said Boy while quickly turning off the computer, "Nothing, just a little school work."

"On a Friday? Are you feeling okay?"

"Uh, yeah, fine."

"Okay, kiddo. Well, I am going to bed. Don't study too hard."

He could not think of a reason to keep him from going to bed, but that could be due to the fact that he found his mind already occupied with thoughts of—well, he couldn't think of his name so he unfolded the paper he had printed out. The bottom half of the man's name had been cut off, it looked like a Ben, or maybe a Dan. Boy decided that he liked Dan much better then Ben, so clearly this man's name must be Dan.

His name was Dan and they—he and Boy—would be married. Boy found himself getting lost the nude man's eyes. They would have two children—no—three children. Two boys and a girl, that way there would be plenty of threats when their daughter went out on dates. I mean imagine it, he laughed quietly to the expression of a guy who was going to take out a girl who lived with four men. Of course two would be gay, maybe more, but Boy hoped his sons wouldn't be gay. In fact he more then hoped, he prayed. It wasn't like he would be angry with them if they were, but it would just be so much easier for them if they were straight.

Dan has amazing eyes, thought Boy. Boy realized that he hadn't looked below Dan's face this entire time, save for the quick glance at his name. But for some reason boy didn't want to. He pulled out a pair of scissors and cut off the bottom half of Dan and threw it in the trash. He did this without looking so it wasn't exactly a straight line. Boy chuckled to himself. "Straight," he chuckled again.

Dan really did have spectacular eyes; one was blue and the other green. Boy was now wondering what Dan's bottom half looked like. He had a right to know, he was married to Dan, he thought. He looked over to the trashcan and looked back to Dan's eyes. Dan was smiling. Boy thought it must have been because of some joke he had told, but he couldn't remember what it was. Suddenly Dan's smile seemed so sad, so lost. Boy knew why. They could never be together, Boy and Dan. After all, Dan was some sort of movie star and all Boy did was bag groceries at a supermarket.

Boy knew that he would have trouble sleeping tonight. ♣

WONDERLUST

Han Yu

the lover i have in my mind
as ideal in this moment
is a woman of fucking grace.
i had wild passionate dreams about this girl i
know
i hooked up with her once at a party
but in my dream i was drawn to her
with a delightful pull inside my astral body
delicious desperation to meld outside of me
like mercury rising to the occasion
and i would flicker to wake state clutching my
blanket
that was just warm skin
or, i would fall awake in my dream
to sublimely do that tantra tango with God
with each intimate breath
          (really, air touches even where sex may not)
so, my lover . . .
i am quite clear that i may not get what i wish
for
and blessed be that
so, my lover . . .

she's a he, maybe. a he-she, she he.
she, he, she's subtly nothing
diva everything
and i say, o just screw it all,
just screw it all down (da halfpipe of desire)

orifices altars
or faces fawning for freedom
sublimely ordinary in our motions
of devotion and desire, decision and delusion
that be, demystifying the illusion
of need, not kneading ourselves into the apple
of our respective eyes

but be free swingin support like clavicle highways
by way of fetishized ideals
like these

so i praise lawd for prose which,
sliced into stanzas,
reveal to my mine that the lover i seek
is not less than the god-of-me
or
any
hot
trick
to be my sweet
all
it
takes
is
someone willing
including me ♣

UNCOVERING

Ellen Freytag

someone once explained to me
that the difference between Dionysian and Apollonian
is the difference between how your stomach turns
and how the pages of a book turn.
i still don't understand that dichotomy,
but i am certain the pages of my stomach
must be flipping furiously now
as i stand face-to-face with the writer
who has just read my soul to me out loud.
the glasses she wore for her reading
are gone now, espresso-warm face framed
only in graying dreads, and i wonder if
i am imagining this recognition as
her eyes look into and through my eyes:
this mutual excavation of the remotest
crevices of veins, dirt under nails,
beads of sweat under arms,
and all the darker chambers.
the superficial seeps so deeply into the spiritual
that i feel like that couple in Paris
who thought they were putting in a kitchen extension
when they dug up the heads of gods
whose bodies, centuries later, were still posed
outside Notre Dame Cathedral

this extension of the writing that has touched my soul
now touching all of me, and all of me
that has ever been. i remember to ask her about
her dreams but cannot speak, and i wonder if
it is because we are both writers that
the incredible calmness of her voice
already my definition of a more-than-thin-white peace
is now magnified larger than truth
in the deep purple instant of her eyes:
the color of a wisdom that has scratched,
even autographed, that place most of us never reach
on the back of peace or god or love.
on the floor of your room,
wrapped in a thin, cotton blanket,
we are completely naked to each other for the first time.
the sweat and skins of our bodies
have never belonged together as much as now,
the smooth and glow of your eyes
rolling back in your head as gently as
the heads of gods
as my hand finds its way deeper inside you
than it has ever been. for minutes,
afterward, when you do not seem
to return my gaze and can say nothing,
i imagine you cannot see nor think of anything
but the color you have just uncovered
with your slowest and most serious smile.
in the morning, when i wake with my lips
tangled in thick, dark rapids of your hair,
you whisper to me that you have dreamt
Alice Walker told you i had beautiful eyes,
and trace the marks your nails have left
on the shadowed small of my back
without apology. ♣

DEAR ANNA

Ellen Freytag

Not everyone can be a letter.
Some of us must bear
the postage in this world.
And though I suppose
we are all the same to you,
today it is finally my turn
to be pulled from the box.

Prostrate on the desk,
your nib cursives across my surface,
the importance of this address
evident in the length of your pause
after each line,
and the acuteness with which
the dots of your i's
press me into oak.
Your breath close upon me
finalizes the paths
your ink has traveled, and then
in my upper right-hand corner
touches down
thirty-three cents worth of adhesive
softened by your kiss.

Turn me over, lift my flap,
insert your pages into my folds,
sliding to my depths.
I tremor as your tongue
snails across the full length
of my inner lip.
Press me to myself,
and I am sealed.
And now I am the one inserted
into cotton folds of your pocket;
clenched fingers, palm sweat
threatening to blur
your careful inscription.
Exposed, trembling again:
you let go;
cool metal grazes my sides;
and I am falling,
recumbent
on a bed of my brothers.

We all bear postage here,
but I find I bear something more:
watermark of a single tear. ♣

SISTER/HERMANA

Wendy M. Thompson

do our bodies look the same?
the eyes, the nose, the cunts.
the pink mouths that open,
that suck
that cry.
you know, I remind you of yourself, li'l girl.
we are not so distant.
or should I say sister?
beautiful brown girl, beautiful sugar swirl.
make me sweet and sticky like you want to
in your mind.
I know what you're thinking you don't have to hide it.
don't be shy.
but you're scared
of what they'll say:
oh, those damned dykes,
those dirty lezbos, those little sluts, hoodrats, skanks, hos, nasty
   dirty whores.
tell me hermanita, will you forget all that if
I open up my heart as soft as a flower and put it in your hands?
the gasp of your warm breath it makes those small hairs on my
   neck tremble.
when you breathe, I can feel that, know what I mean?
they say gayness is bad, but it is worse for us.

for us two crazy halfbreed girls
two cultures and worlds colliding in one orgasmic moment.
they say we're pretty much fucked up.
confused.
existing without pricks.
fucking with plastic dicks.
yeah, its pretty bad, babygirl.
but you will not worry when I come to you in that Technicolor
    dream.
you won't shy away when I reach for you.
no.
not like on the bus when I wanted to tell you so badly, "Mija, can
    I be with you for a long time? can we be more than just friends?
can I make love to you until you can't take it anymore?"
I am still waiting.
the picture playing out in perfect reality,
my mind asking over and over, "Should I do it now?"
and you will lean over on purpose
your breasts teasing playfully, falling from the lip of your shirt and
    say, "Yea." with no shame, no apprehension, no sound. ♣

TALKING DIRTY

Alicia Brooks

As her hand moves up my thigh, she leans in close and whispers the two sexiest words in the English language: "Show me." Despite a considerable level of experience, this is the most I have ever talked during sex. She wastes no time in telling me what she wants and asking me what I like. When I find the right spot, she lets me know unmistakably. For the first time in four years of college, I worry about waking my neighbors. I have never been this uninhibited before. With my other lovers, I was virtually silent, but that all changes with her. I tell her how much I love her body, how sexy she is when she comes, how the thought of kissing her has distracted me all day. When she says "show me," I take her hand and guide it without a moment's hesitation. The lights are on and I am not the least bit ashamed of my body. She and I are not in love. We barely know each other. This is not a comfort level born of emotional intimacy. It is the simple fact of her openness. I thought that a sex-positive

dyke like me was beyond feeling ashamed. Yet her complete lack of shame peels away layers of my own that have been hidden for years. There is no shame in knowing how I like to be touched. There is no shame in wanting to touch her. There is no shame in being a woman who desires another woman. ♣

BE OKAY (*lyrics*)

Alicia Champion

I knocked on your door just the other day
I had missed your smile and I wanted to play
But you weren't there, you had gone away
Now I've given you reasons to take your space
I've given you love in tasteless ways
I've given you more than you can take

But now the sun is still out and it's seven p.m.
My shades are pulled, I'm hiding in
I guess I'm just scared to find you and hear you
say,
"I'll be okay"

You came to me at a time when I thought I had it all
Had my sanity intact, my heart in my hands
And the wisdom from every past rise and fall
New bridges are built while others burn down
But if no one is there, will they still make a sound?
If I'm hurting alone, am I hurting at all?
Am I pretending to be happy or pretending to be sad?
Does it really make a difference as long as I have
The one thing I need, which is everything to get
along with my life ♣

So I'll be okay
I'll be okay
If you saw me today, what would you see
Would that rainbow above us diminish into the
Lightning storms that we can be
Maybe you won't react anymore
You've OD'd on my drug and are too numb
To open up any more doors

The part of you that thought you're in love with me
Was the only part of you that loved me at all
And now that you're sure you're not anymore
There's nothing to be said between these walls

But I'll be okay
I'll be okay
I knocked on your door just the other day
I had missed your smile ♣

COLD WAR (*lyrics*)

Alicia Champion and Caroline Boehmer

Lonely sets this sun
Upon the arrival of your chosen one
A moonless sky quilts the night
Restless slumber fills me with fright
I'm baffled by my mind
It's lost control and's been so unkind
And pushes us away
Or maybe I'm too frightened to say . . .

That I'm not in love with you
And I don't know what I've got to prove
'Cause free is the love
Inside of me
But I'm not in love with you

Waiting through still water days
Tempted and tortured in undefined ways
And I can't hold you tonight
But don't be fooled
It's a cold war to fight
You won't see the love that I show
So many oceans, how could we have known
And you won't see this longing I face
Until I show you
You can't be replaced

I'm not in love with you
And I don't know what you want me to prove
'Cause free is the love
Inside of me
But I'm not in love with you

You pull a string in my heart
That never knew it could love
Before I can even betray
I feel you running away

I've known you for this long
And lies make you believe I am strong
If this is our final end
Then I am fighting just to pretend

That I'm not in love with you
And I don't know who I'm trying to fool
'Cause free is the love
Inside of me
But I'm not in love with you
Not in love with you
Not in love with you ♣

SWAY

Lauren Adler

Her hands touch my waist
Move to the rhythm
Knee bent
Curves and sways
My body moves out of sway
Then I find my solitude
I curve and sway
I sing
I shout
I find her, and we dance
I sway
I twirl
With comfort
Strange comfort
That I move
And sway
And sing ♣

FISH FOOD (*lyrics*)

Alicia Champion

Life's kinda funny in its traditional ways
And I'm living here in these not so traditional days
But still it's hard to find all that's true
Still it's tough to be the one and only you
So I'm just here living in that place with him
He uses me when he needs
I'm the food off which he feeds
I don't have a choice
I've kinda lost my voice
Well I guess it's up to me
It's my choice to be free
And
By the way
Where am I gonna stay?
Don't really wanna hear what he has to say
Down on my luck
My chances are slim
Looks like I'm staying another night
As fish food with him
And
So I'm walking down the street and there she stands
She saw me over there and she returned my stare
She could tell from my face, the thoughts in my head

With her seductive smile my whole face turned red
She said,
And
By the way
Where're you gonna stay?
I said, don't really wanna hear what the world has to say
She said, well my door's wide open
Why don't you come right on in?
I'll give you something that you're never gonna get
Staying over there with him
And
And she lifted me up
She let me see
That I was foolish, not to believe
And of everything I'd never known
It was clearer now
Now that I's shown

Now that I's shown
And
So I went back to that boyfriend
Told him I found someone else
He asked me why, I said simply she was kind
He said, she?? To a girl you're gonna part?
So what the hell's she giving you?
And I said a heart and he said,
And
By the way
Where're you gonna stay?
And I said, don't really care what you and the world have to say
Her door's wide open I'm gonna walk right on in
She gave me something I's never gonna get staying over here
    with . . .
By the way
Where're you gonna stay?

Don't really care what the world has to say
She said,
Well my door's wide open, why don't you come right on in
I'll give you something that you're never gonna get
Staying over there with him. ♣

ONE TWO

Holden Jude Dean

Your smile seems less crooked now
But maybe I just forgot the
Imperfections of your teeth
Because it's been so long since
I last traced them with my tongue
Or maybe I just can't see
Past that gray color your
Eyes seem to be drowning in
It doesn't really matter
Because your mouth doesn't
Belong to me anymore
And your hopscotch heartbeat
Doesn't match mine like it
Used to [onetwo onetwo]
When we'd sink in heavy
Winter silence breathing
Conversation on the windowpanes
Your smile seems less crooked now
And it makes me want to break your jaw ♣

ONETWOTHREE

Holden Jude Dean

She says car crashes aren't beautiful
But I'd have to disagree
There's just something so symphonic
About the way metal meets bone meets earth
And all kept time by the heartbeat
Tired metronome
It kind of reminds me of you
And the way my flesh meets yours
Inevitable and filled with casual
Brutality ♣

Section Six

[INTERVIEWS]

BRADEN JAHR

Braden Jahr, 16, was gay bashed at his Michigan high school. After dropping out for months, he returned stronger than ever. Now he runs the queer teen website Broder13.com and organizes a diversity youth group on campus.

Tell me about your hometown and how the harassment started.

I grew up in a very small town in rural Michigan called Sebewaing, which has approximately 2,000 residents. It was generally a pleasant place for me to grow up in, up until the last few years that is. Diversity is not accepted, diversity in this town is bowling on Tuesdays instead of Saturdays. The word "gay" is rarely used nicely and close-minded locals have driven out the only African-American families that have moved here. It really is a pity for anyone diverse to live here. It also closets a lot of GLBT people. As long as I can remember I have spoken my mind, eventually I told people, sometimes the *wrong* people, that I was gay. It wasn't even something I had struggled with—I just knew, I had always known. Unfortunately, many people cannot understand that.

Since kindergarten I went to a parochial school, very religious, where I was taught that homosexuality is an abomination. I graduated from the eighth grade . . . and very soon my ninth grade year started out at the public high school. On the second day I was walking down the hall and a young male said the word, the word that wounds every gay teenager: "fag." From there on in things snowballed. Daily more and more people would use those hate words, fag, homo, queer, sissy. Eventually things moved from words, to violence and pranks. The word "faggot" (it was misspelled by the way) was written on the locker next to mine, only because they made a mistake of which locker it was. There were more things that happened, but I really do not think it is necessary to name them all.

Can you tell me a bit more about how you felt those first few weeks after your attack?

I was very distraught. Suicidal even . . . I hated my life. I felt like the world hated me. I was very angry and very sad; a whirlwind of emotions. On February 13th, 2001, I was attacked in the hallway. I do not remember much of it, as my head was hit on the locker several times and I must have blacked out or something. That was the last day of school for me. I withdrew from high school that I had attended for only six months. The school did "the best they could do" as they put it. In my mind little was done. For a month I stayed in bed, scared, depressed, angry, and even suicidal at times. The school did not offer to help with schooling, or even make the effort to call and see how I was doing. During the time I was there I had had a few organizations in to talk with them and it did work, for awhile. After I left I looked for a lawyer. I called the American Civil Liberties Union. I did everything I could to help to fix the school. In time, I realized that suing wasn't the answer.

Why did you eventually decide that suing wasn't the answer?

I do not know. That wasn't really *my* decision. A lawyer and my mother thought that it was best. I didn't argue.

How did your parents react to all of this?

I haven't talked with my father in four years . . . my mother was, to say the least, very upset that this happened to me. My mother sent a few strongly worded letters to the school and even visited them a few times.

Then what happened?

I managed to get the courage to go back into the school and meet with the administration. Because of that, I have founded a diversity group, and I have also set many goals for the school to achieve. I have also realized that the school isn't as bad as I thought it was and the school has been very supportive recently. Then again, maybe that was because of my constant pressure on them to be supportive. Since then I have worked hard to become a gay rights advocate.

What's the response been like to the diversity group you founded—both from teachers and students?

It is very mixed. A lot of the teachers are a bit skittish about the entire idea, and the student body has many different views on it.

Why do you think you survived all that?

In retrospect, I need to thank a lot of people for keeping me alive. If I had never gone through some of the struggles in my life prior to these high school incidents I probably wouldn't be here. I would have committed suicide. I was lucky. So many innocent teenagers go through this same kind of thing; many end their own lives because of the ignorance out in the world. I mean, if high school is like this, what is the rest of the world like? ♣

KATIE KAPUT

Katie Kaput is a 21-year-old trans parent living in the San Francisco Bay Area with her boyfriend, Ricky, and her son, Rio.

Can you tell us a little bit about your coming-out—how did you find a trans community, and how did you find a dyke community that welcomed trans women?

I came out as a queer trans girl when I was 13, but it wasn't until I was 15 that I found any sort of queer community. In Chicago, I found my way into a dyke community that was comprised mostly of people only a few years older than me who were really into queer punk music. Most of my friends at that time were involved in the Chicago Lesbian Avengers, as was I. They were very welcoming to me as a trans girl when I first got involved, even though at the time I don't think anyone else in the group was out as trans. I had been communicating with the Avengers for a little while, trying to figure out whether I would really feel safe and comfortable in their space, and at the first meeting I attended, some people even referred to me as their "favorite baby dyke." I was so excited and flattered. That was really the first time I felt like non-trans people were validating my girl and dyke identities.

Still, I felt really nervous at the meeting. I suggested we attend and help organize Camp Trans 1999, a protest against the exclusion of trans women at the Michigan Womyn's Music Festival. Even though I had known these people for a long time, I didn't feel sure I could trust them to care about my inclusion more than some of the bands that they liked who were playing. I also knew several of them were planning to attend the festival. People were very supportive and we went to Camp Trans that year, where my activism consisted of bursting into tears when I was surrounded by a number of shouting anti-inclusion festies who really seemed ready to commit violence against me.

I've never really found a trans community, although I have had many friends who are trans men or boys or genderqueer people. I've always felt like being a trans girl has made me stick out in a major way in the sort of trans spaces I've ended up in, or the dyke-focused-but-trans-inclusive spaces I've been in.

How can dyke communities be more welcoming to trans women?

Don't support the exclusion of trans women from women's spaces. Make sure your trans-positive spaces are transGIRLpositive, too, not just trans boy positive—although I know many trans boys who feel very uncomfortable in those spaces. Never accuse someone of having . . . male energy, residual or otherwise. All that does is put trans women in the same position most women are in, only doubled because of being both women and trans, the position of being somehow bad or threatening if they ever speak up for themselves, but simultaneously weak or, in the case of trans women specifically, copying sexist stereotypes if we give in to all your demands and let you say whatever you want. We can't do anything right in that situation.

When and why did you decide to parent?

I always knew I wanted to be a parent someday. When I met my boyfriend Ricky—who is also trans—everything came together. We both wanted to be parents and we both had some amount of urgency over the fact that we wanted change our bodies a lot in ways that might not be compatible with being biological parents. So I stopped taking my hormones and we hoped for the best. And now we have a beautiful son named Rio Francesco. Trans queer teen parenting has been very rewarding.

Society often has bad reactions to people choosing to parent when they are young, let alone queer and trans. How has your decision to parent been received?

Some of my friends are now considering having children of their own! Some others seem to think I'm making a mistake, and that I'll never have time to do anything cool or worthwhile. Not only is Rio worthwhile and cool and then some, but also I'm much more productive in my use of my free time than I was before becoming a parent. Everything feels much more cool and worthwhile and valuable, not less. My family didn't really care one way or the other. My parents have seven kids of their own; they just had another recently and they started fairly young. I've been less involved in activism since Rio was born . . . which is partly due to logistics. But I'm going to be much more involved as he grows up. He is such an inspiration. I look at his face and I don't want him to ever have to deal with all the crap in the world, and then I want that for all the other babies out there, too.

How do you and your partner handle your gender and sexual identities as it relates to raising your child?

We're just planning to be very open with Rio about gender and sexuality, and supportive of any feelings he has about his own gender or sexuality. There hasn't been much of a reaction from "professionals" so far, but he isn't even two yet, so we'll see. Mostly we just get what I expected: parents pulling their kids away from us or Rio at the playground, parents or kids saying rude things. ♣

AMBER LAYTON

Amber Layton is a 14-year-old lesbian in Orlando, Florida.

How old were you when you began to come out?

I was 12 when I came out to myself. I started coming out to my friends when I was 13, and my parents just figured it out on their own. I was about 13 when they said something to me up front, but I'm sure they [knew earlier].

Is it hard being out at 14?

I don't find it hard because all my friends are supportive and the fact that I still have friends and I am out means a lot to me. My parents are really cool, so that helps me out, too. The thing that I do find challenging is dealing with those immature "popular" people who don't have a clue and just call me "lesbian" and "dyke." All the people who do say crap like that to me are people I was friends with in elementary school. It hurts.

Do you know any other queer youth around your age?

I only know one person who is a lesbian. I have a couple of friends who are bisexual—they're all girls.

I remember that it was really frustrating to be out and young, and feel like even in the queer youth community, people were a lot older than I was. How do you handle that age difference?

I find that to be frustrating as well, because here you are this 12, 13 year old, and no one takes you as serious as you want them to. You know what you want and who you are but people say, "No, you don't know what you want. You're just this little kid who doesn't know what you want or what you're talking about." That pisses me off. The other thing that got to me was that I didn't have anyone to love. You see all your friends with their boyfriends going around holding hands, but you can't do that with anyone. I felt left out. And I had gotten used to not having anyone, because I wasn't going to go out with guys just because they were there. I had no one else. I knew what I wanted, so when I finally got myself out there and found people who had the same feelings I did, I was so excited.

How did you meet your current girlfriend?

I met her at school. She came out to me, and eventually I asked her out.

How have your parents handled you coming out?

My parents are so cool about it all. My mom was actually the one who exposed me to the gay community. I knew what gay was and everything, but I didn't really understand it all. It wasn't until my mom dragged me along to see the Indigo Girls that I actually got to see what the whole thing was about. The Butchies were the opening band, and I was like, "Mom, that guy is cute." It was really the lead singer Kaia! My mom said, "That's a girl," and I'm thinking, "Ooh, she's still hot!" After that all that was in my CD player were the Indigo Girls, The Butchies, k.d. lang, Melissa Etheridge, Tegan and Sara. That's probably around the time my parents started to suspect something was up. My dad is really awesome with it as well. I thought he would have taken it worse [than my mom], but he's the one who is driving me all around town just for me to see my girlfriend. I love my parents for everything they have done for me, and I don't think I would be who I am right now if it wasn't for them. ♣

MATHILDA MINERVA

MAHAL DE DIOS

Mathilda Minerva Mahal de Dios is a 21-year-old queer hybrid Filipina who lives in Colorado Springs, Colorado. She's currently working on Ways Out Academy's Projecto Libertad, a program to enhance literacy and cultural competency in kids ages nine to 14.

What kinds of issues do you face trying to offer a multi-cultural education to these youth?

The kids from Ways Out Academy are all Latina/o. We just finished the poetry collaborative in which the tutors and the students from Ways Out were all student-teacher-poets. We based our workshops on Paulo Friere's *Pedagogy of the Oppressed* and June Jordan's *Poetry for the People*. Even though my friend Maria and I were co-leaders for the poetry program, we still did the same exercises as the rest of the workshop participants. We encouraged the kids to use whichever language they were most comfortable using. I am not yet able to speak Spanish, but because Maria can we were able to create an environment that was more comfortable.

What do enjoy about working with youth?

I love working with youth because the process of connecting with young people gives me the opportunity to connect with myself.

The last day of the program I cried because several of the kids articulated their joy and frustration in ways that I had never heard. Some of them had not spoken in class before, and by the end of the program they were performance poets.

You are also working with the Purple Rose Campaign, an international campaign against the sex trafficking of Filipinas worldwide.

I want people to recognize that our struggles are interconnected. Patriarchy, sexism, heterosexism, and globalization are all root causes of this particular form of exploitation. This issue affects me, especially when newspapers advertise mail-order brides, or when people tell me that they have a "thing" for Asian girls. It is also necessary to recognize that the imperialist relationship of the U.S in the Philippines perpetuates the exploitation. Militarization of the Philippines continues through the Visiting Forces Agreement and the U.S refuses to recognize that its legacy of toxic pollution in the Philippines has violated international laws. The Purple Rose Campaign comes out of the need to heighten awareness around sex trafficking and the root causes of exploitation.

You are also planning a series of political education workshops for an upcoming hip-hop festival that will heighten awareness about the prison industrial complex. What do you hope people will learn from your workshops?

The prison industrial complex has its roots in the overcrowding of Immigration and Naturalization Services detention centers. The criminalization of people, especially people of color, clearly shows that institutional racism feeds other systems of oppression.

What about hip-hop organizing is appealing to you?

I grew up listening to hip hop, and while there is misogyny, homophobia, and classism rampant throughout, I am reminded that there are so many artists and activists that are leaders of this hip hop generation. I remember growing up listening to lyrics that spoke true to my life. There is something not only irresistible but also celebratory about activism. The strength of community lies within our power to release with imaginative self-statement. ♣

IOLANTA STAR

Iolanta Star is the pen name of a 16-year-old Russian immigrant lesbian.

Tell me about coming to the U.S. from Russia.

I am from a very small—about one square mile long—scientific town about 50 miles Southwest of Moscow. It is called Puschino. I moved to the U.S. in 1998. My dad came here to work at Penn State University; he has a Ph.D. in Molecular Biology and he's currently working here as a postdoctoral researcher. My mom is technically a cellular biologist, but after we came here, she was going more or less crazy because of having to sit all day at home so eventually she got a job in my dad's lab although this is actually not her real specialty. I also have a sister, who is two years younger than I am. I do still have most of my relatives in Russia—both pairs of grandparents, aunt, uncles, and cousins. This summer, I got a chance to visit them in Russia for the first time since we moved here. That was rather nice. I also got a chance to see all the places I've been at when I grew up, and I got to see my best friend, Dasha, who currently lives with her family in California and came to Russia this summer for a visit as well.

Do you want to go back when you're older?

Actually, I'm not quite sure. The economic situation in Russia is quite shady at the moment so I suppose it would not be wise to return right now. There's also the problem of having to pass the examinations in Russian and Literature if I was to enroll in a Russian university, and though I could probably pass the former, the latter would definitely kill me. Consequently, I am currently in the process of applying to Penn State. That would simply be easier. I would like to get a green card eventually (visas are rather troublesome), but even if I could, I would not want to become a U.S. citizen. I feel like that could be equated with in a way betraying my true nationality whereas with a green card, I would be able to go to Russia any time I want. I think my future more or less lies in the U.S., but I don't want to lose the tie with Russia, either.

What was it like when you first arrived here?

In the fall of 1998, Russia experienced a very sharp economic downfall. My father actually left for America a couple of months before that, but when the country entered an economic depression, we simply could not stay there for long because it was nearly impossible to survive on my mom's salary—although her salary was considered an average one. We flew on a plane first from Moscow to Helsinki, and then from Helsinki to New York City, where my dad picked us up on a rented car. I'd been in the U.S. before—we spent a couple of months in Kansas when I was nine years old—so the plane flights weren't anything new to me. My sister and I had to take an English proficiency test there and I ended up in an Advanced ESL group while she entered the Beginner ESL one. The ESL teacher was constantly giving some sort of parties for every holiday imaginable and I learned very little English that year. The science and math classes were very easy since my Russian program has covered them long ago. I only got back on the right track in high school, when I tested out of ESL and got, by pure accident, into an advanced English class. The high school classes are a lot more challenging especially since I take all the advanced ones. I was a very good student in Russia, and I sort of lost track of this feeling of intelligence in eigth grade, and found it again when I discovered that I was actually rather good in all of the classes I took during my freshman year and from then forth. I am currently in the top ten percent of the class.

Do you know any other gay people at your school?

Well, I live in central Pennsylvania. Some sort of politician—I don't remember who exactly—once said that in Pennsylvania, there is Pittsburgh on one side, Philadelphia on the other, and Alabama in the middle. So I can honestly say that I don't know any gay students. However, there are rumors going around about some of the teachers. I was lucky to have classes with one of those teachers for every year up to this one. I'm really not sure whether or not that teacher is a lesbian. I do know that she is very nice and I still visit her sometimes, but I would not want to come out to her just in case she is not really a lesbian. I am not quite sure whether to regard it as fortunate that I had a gay teacher during my sophomore year. I did not know he was gay then, but I did like his style of teaching. Needless to say, it came as a huge disappointment when he was discovered at the end of that year having sex with a male student in a public bathroom. Some role model! That was so wrong, and on so many different levels. Last year I had a teacher, who is quite obviously a lesbian because she is so very butch; plus she knows a lot about GLBT current events, and that is always a good indication. Throughout the year, she kept making us write personal journals, etc., and I must have annoyed her quite a lot by mentioning my sexuality in nearly every single one of them and doing my American author project on Nancy Garden. In my yearbook, the teacher wrote that I kept the year interesting for her and I am still not sure whether to take that as a compliment or as an insult.

Do you worry about coming out to your parents?

I am not quite sure how my parents would react. They are rather homophobic, but not as homophobic as they technically could have been. I mean I'm sure they would not throw me out or do anything else as extreme. Since I am not quite comfortable with either coming out or lying to them, I almost subconsciously tried to balance both. They would have to be really dense not to suspect anything. I've tried asking them, as tacitly as I possibly could, about their opinions on homosexuality. The responses were not quite encouraging. But at least my Mom did watch *Buffy the Vampire Slayer* with me, and there is a positive lesbian character, so I'm kind of hoping that made her at least a little bit more tolerant. I'm mostly afraid of coming out because that would create many difficulties in my relationship with my parents and, being the perfectionist that I am, I don't feel capable of creating more problems that I would have to deal with. At least not until I meet someone who will be worth it. I do know that this is merely an excuse, but I'm truly horrified of coming out to them.

Do you think being an immigrant makes coming out harder?

Not really. I think coming out is always difficult. However, there is a difference that I suppose was caused by me being from another country. Greatly due to my insecurities with my English-speaking abilities . . . I became sort of an outcast. I am one of those kids who is nice to everyone, but close to no one. This did not have a positive effect on my social skills. I'm simply not sure whether or not I can be open with other people about something as personal as my sexuality. I feel a need to keep my feelings to myself even as I don't want to lie. It's sort of like I want people to know, but without myself actually telling them.

Do you get to interact with other queer people at all?

I went to a Lambda Student Alliance meeting at Penn State last year. Technically, it's a university group, but they do allow the community people to come as well. I did not meet anyone personally there, but it was really nice, just talking with a bunch of people who are definitely not homophobic about gay issues. I liked it. If I go to Penn State next year, I'm going to become a member. However, the problem last year was trying to explain to my parents afterwards why it was that I came home at nine p.m. and, as I said, I don't like lying to my parents. It would be easier next year when I'm going to have more freedom to manage my time as I see fit. I communicate with some of the other gay people over the Internet, but, unfortunately, the e-mail serve groups generally tend to slowly die out after about a month or two of heightened activity so electronic communication does have its own flaws. ♣

KRYSTAL BENNETT

Krystal Bennett, 19, was elected prom king at her high school in Ferndale, Washington in 2002. It caused quite a stir. She now lives in Blaine, Washington.

Why did you run for Prom King?

Honestly, I didn't think about it. A friend of mine was joking that she didn't want to vote for any of the guys because they were all jerks, and I joked, "Well, you could vote for me." It caught on from that. It wasn't a set idea or plan, and it wasn't meant to turn into something political. It just happened.

The reaction to you becoming prom king seemed to have as much to do with traditional gender roles as it did with your sexuality—after you won, people talked about creating a school policy to designate that future prom kings will be male and queens female. Can you talk a little about the intersections between homophobia and fear of people who express their gender in a non-traditional way?

When all of this happened, I was interviewed in our local paper, and the woman who wrote the article mentioned that I was a lesbian several times. But this wasn't about me being queer. This was about me being comfortable. People who were against it were responding with "Being gay is wrong." And I'd say, "I didn't run because I'm a lesbian" and then they'd respond, "Well, you shouldn't have run because you're a girl." I ran because prom 'king' is the title I'm most comfortable under. Tiaras and roses don't suit me. I have a problem with people being forced into gender categories, and to assume that every girl wants to wear a dress and have roses makes me mad. For the people here, the two issues [gender and sexuality] were inseparable. But I didn't run because I'm a lesbian. I ran because it was what I was comfortable with.

After you won Prom King, you got a lot of national media attention. There were articles about you in numerous newspapers and magazines, and Reverend Fred Phelps staged a protest of your high school graduation. What was it like to suddenly be the target of someone like Phelps?

It was really scary. A lot of the people here had no clue who he was. When people heard about it, the response was basically, "That sucks, what a jerk." I would explain, "No, you don't understand what a jerk he is, this man celebrated the death of Matthew Shepard," and they would ask, "Who's Matthew Shepard?" It was amazing to see how ignorant people were. For four years, I was the only openly gay student at the school. I've spent four years trying to educate people at my school. I got books with gay characters into the school library, and this year I finally got the *Advocate* into the library. That took four years. I go to prom the way that I'm comfortable, and then I'm the target of hatred, and I had to explain to these people who was targeting me! It was a never-ending cycle of them having no clue.

Has the Ferndale community been at all supportive of you? Do you plan to stay in Ferndale?

There are some really great people here who have given me a lot of support, people who understand. But generally, Ferndale has been pretty terrible. There were concerned parents calling my school after I won prom king, and it was suggested that I not walk during graduation because I would be "putting people in danger." I decided to walk, and I suggested that the administration put up metal detectors because of the "safety issue" and they said no. So it would be all right if someone came in with a gun and shot me, but me "endangering" other students by walking would be a problem. My mom and my sister took days off work to go to the school to make sure I'd be kept safe. I'm not staying in Ferndale. I'm thinking about moving to San Francisco and studying at the Academy of Art College. In the long run, I'm going to move out of here.

What kind of art do you do?

I do everything! I have a few favorite pieces: a plaster mold of my sister's belly with a picture of a fetus shellaqued over the belly button; a ceramic hand gun with the face of a young child and the words "Queer youth are seven times more likely to commit suicide" carved into it; a painting of the Matthew Shepard . . . crouching on the steps, and the sky and the building transposed with the fence where he was found. I'm also interested in studying law and social justice. At Western Washington University they have a major in Gay, Lesbian, Bisexual, and Transgender Studies, so I could basically get an activism degree. ♣

JULIE HENDERSON

Julie Henderson, 16, is a junior at Woodside Priory, a Catholic school in Portola Valley, California. She is fighting to keep a Gay-Straight Alliance, which has been banned by the Archdiocese of San Francisco.

Has the Archdiocese given you any reasons for banning the club?

The Archdiocese has not made any statements concerning the existence of GSAs in Catholic schools. Archbishop Levada is extremely conservative, and has estranged himself from the gay and lesbian community in the Bay Area. It wasn't until recently that the Archdiocese even acknowledged GSAs. When I first heard that we were not going to be able to start our club this year, I wrote a letter to the Archbishop asking him if he could offer us some insight concerning the dismissal of our club. I have not received a response.

What has the student response to the GSA been?

People support our cause. We began a petition and collected signatures from two-thirds of the high school students and a notable amount of faculty as well. We have informed the students and faculty about our struggle by word of mouth, since we are not allowed to advertise our club on campus. Everyone is outraged. People want to see this through.

Do the students at Woodside have any say in what the fate of the club will be?

Unfortunately, the students do not have final say as to what the fate of our club will be. However, we all have the power to spread the news, and we can inform our communities of our struggle. It all comes down to whether or not the Archbishop gives us the "Okay, go." And at present, that does not seem very likely. Since we are an independent Catholic high school, we are not subject to laws that would otherwise protect our efforts to start this club. The church is trying to avoid controversy as much as possible, especially considering all of the recent sexual abuse allegations against clergy members.

How do you think the church's silence around sexual issues plays into how your GSA is being treated?

I absolutely feel that the church is trying to draw the least amount of attention to itself at the moment. That last thing the church needs on its hands is a student-waged revolution against Roman Catholic-inspired homophobia. I think that it is time for the church to wake up and acknowledge the fact that the times have changed since the last Vatican Council that was held nearly fifty years ago. The church has never admitted to faults committed and is renowned for being extremely "hush hush" when covering up for its members. As a result of the church's purposeful neglect to address the issue, students of varying sexual identities and backgrounds who attend Catholic schools are forced to suffer in silence and seek support elsewhere. Who is in the right: a clergy member molests a young child who is then scarred for life, or a group of students who are trying to make a positive difference in their community by establishing a club that promotes diversity? It is a decision that the Church will have to attest to on its own. Until then, I will continue to take refuge in the philosophy of the Catholic Church, which is that it embraces all members of God's family. ♣

BUNNY G

Bunny G, 19, founded the Hampshire College chapter of Radical Cheerleaders—a group that blends activism with cheerleading. She lives in Amherst, Massachusetts.

What is Radical Cheerleaders? How did the group get started?

Radical Cheerleaders was started by two girls named Amy and Cara in 1996. They started it because they wanted a more interesting way to do activism. Radical Cheerleading gets more attention than a lot of other activism, and it has a sense of humor about itself. A year ago I heard about the group from a friend of mine. I decided to start one at Hampshire because there's a lot of activism here, but people also get frustrated with traditional approaches to activism sometimes.

How is this different from other kinds of activism?

It's really important to remember that Radical Cheerleaders are activists, not just performance artists or people who are being silly. We are inherently a radical group and we support radical leftist causes. For some people this is an introduction to activism, but a lot of us have been activists before Radical Cheerleading, too. Even if we stop being Radical Cheerleaders, we're still activists.

How do you write the cheers?

Each squad doesn't write all its own cheers all the time. There's a cheer book that was written by Amy and Cara that's full of a lot of really awesome cheers. When the Hampshire squad does write its own cheers, it's usually for a specific event, like a peace rally or pro-choice demonstration or anti-racism march. Three or four people will get together and come up with ideas, and we'll try to write something funny that still gets the message across.

Who is cheering with Radical Cheerleaders?

Anyone is allowed to join Radical Cheerleaders. We're open to all genders. Athletic ability has nothing to do with whether or not you can join. We all have a similar radical political stance.

Since the war in Iraq began, fear of terrorism has risen dramatically, and many radical left-wing activists have talked about the fear of being labeled "terrorist-sympathizers" because they don't support the war. How do you feel the war has affected activists in this country?

Ever since this happened, Hampshire Radical Cheerleaders has basically gone to a peace rally each week. The mainstream media says that 90 percent of the American people support the war, but I just don't think that's true. We went to a rally in Boston and there were 500 people there chanting for peace and justice. Recently we were cheering at a rally in Amherst, and a guy in a car pulled up and started yelling at us, "What would you do? Five thousand innocent people died? What would you do?" It's really hard to respond to something like that, but I asked him, "Why do more people have to die?" Another 5,000 people will probably die in Afghanistan, but of course people aren't thinking of that because it doesn't hit as close to home.

Do you have any advice for people who want to start or join a Radical Cheerleaders chapter?

There's a national listserv on the Internet (www.groups. yahoo.com/group/radicalcheers), so if you want to start a squad, it's a good idea to get on that list. Also, remember that every squad is autonomous and you can do things your own way. ♣

[CONTRIBUTORS]

Lauren Adler, 19, of Doylestown, Pennsylvania dreams of clouds, contra dancing, and a place called Falcon Ridge. She is pursuing her ever-evolving happiness and discovery of self. She has the tiniest handwriting known to (wo)man. Lauren is learning splendiferous and magnanimous things at Smith College in Northampton, Massachusetts.

Sherisse Alvarez is currently in her final year at Hampshire College in Amherst, Massachusetts. She is studying yoga and womanist artistic practice through photography, video and performance. She recently completed a memoir titled *The Back and Forth of Passing*. Sherisse has read her work at The New School, Bluestockings Bookstore, Brooklyn College, Untitled Space Gallery and Food for Thought Books.

R.L. Baldwin, from Atlanta, Georgia, has a strong desire to destroy the stereotypes that divide the black gay and straight communities. His upcoming works are sure to create quite a stir on both sides of the issue. He can be reached at rlbaldwin2000@aol.com.

Amy Bell is a 21-year-old student, writer, freelance journalist, artist, activist, and all-around kick-ass chick from Leicester, England. Amy helped organize the 2000 Gay Pride event in her hometown, and recently established a local feminist group. She is currently a philosophy major at the University of Warwick in the UK, and is trying in vain to write her first novel in between studies and—well, other things. She is an

avid fan of old black-and-white movies, modern art, Polly
Harvey, *The Simpsons*, and cinnamon and raisin bagels.

Alicia Brooks is a 23-year-old graduate of Bryn Mawr College
living in Annapolis, Maryland. She works on Maryland's
Eastern Shore as a mentor for children with mental health
needs. Outside of work, she teaches Sunday school,
volunteers for PFLAG, facilitates a GLBT book club called
Out of Print Annapolis, and recently co-founded the under-
30 GLBT social/political group "Out in Naptown." She
first read this essay at Mothertongue, a women's spoken
word event in Washington, D.C.. You can contact her at
peechez@rocketmail.com.

Alicia Elizabeth Champion, 21, was born in Singapore where
she spent the first ten years of her life. Her mother, Valerie
Barth, was a trained classical pianist and her father, Charles
Champion, was a practicing musician/ performer whose name
was common in the arts and culture scene in Singapore
throughout the seventies and eighties. In 1991 Alicia moved
to San Francisco, California. By 17, when she had been
performing music for several years, she self-engineered and
produced her debut release, *Stories of My Soul*, under her
newly founded independent record label, Champ Records.
She attended Berklee College of Music where she recorded
her self-produced, sophomore release, *Cold Wars*. She has
since shared the stage with artists such as Sophie B. Hawkins,
Alix Olson, Doria Roberts, Nick Name and Acid Nine. Along
with performing and self-producing, Alicia also has produced
other artists under the Champ Records label such as *RENT*
star Kevin Wood.

Arielle Davis is a silly 25-year-old female writer, student, political
questioner, spirituality seeker, meat-eating pagan, Internet
junkie, beach-lovin' feminist mama (in no particular order)
in Tampa, Florida. She identifies as bisexual most of the time,
unless she's feeling queer. She lives with her boyfriend/
unofficial husband of five years and their beautiful 18-month-
old daughter. She is once again back in school at USF

pursuing her English degree with a minor in Women's Studies and enjoys being back out in the world again after her two-year hiatus of pregnancy and nursing.

Holden Jude Dean is a 19-year-old genderqueer transboy from Vancouver, British Columbia. He has a proclivity towards self-destructive behavior and thrusts himself into chaotic situations at every opportunity. He lives on music, poetry, pinprick starry nights, and very little sleep. Currently attempting to complete a somewhat-second year of university, Holden lives with his two biggest loves: his girlfriend, Zandara and their cat Ginsburg. He plans on running far, far away with his skateboard and some paper as soon as summer hits. He has been writing seriously for roughly two years and aspires to be a starving artist when he's done being a starving student.

Lauren Eve comes from the D.C./Maryland/Virginia area and currently goes to school in Delaware. She is studying child development and women's studies, and hopes to combine the two in creating a curriculum that encourages a gender-neutral classroom. She is also active in LGBT and women's issues and recently organized a Rock for Choice concert at the University of Delaware. She loves music, books, and finding beauty in the oddest places. This is her first time being published.

Ellen Freytag is a 20-year-old genderqueer dyke and a Stanford junior who would major in poetry if she could. She edits *Masque* magazine, a journal for queer expression, and *Fire!*, a publication of Stanford's LGBT Community Resources Center. This is not her first (or last) time in print.

Nadine Gartner is a strong Jewish dyke who graduated magna cum laude from Bryn Mawr College. After living and working in New York City for two years, she enrolled in the University of Michigan Law School. Upon completion of her degree, Nadine plans to devote her life to queer activism. Her mother continues to be very proud of her.

James Patrick Gillece III, a recent high school graduate, moved from Baltimore to New York City for college where he hopes to major in English and continue to write.

sandra* Henderson is an 18-year-old lesbian-thespian-poet from Ontario, Canada. Besides attempting to label herself for bios such as these, sandra spends her time searching for answers and attempting to be spontaneous.

Rachel Kasa, 21, is a self-identified queer artist/writer. Her short stories and poetry have been published in *Cherry Bleeds*, *Comrades*, *MsFit Magazine* and *Pussy Power*. She likes redheaded boy-girls, mint ice cream, semiotics and Milan Kundera. She doesn't like Hollywood blockbusters made from her favorite books; Barbara Streisand; or fundamentalist Christians (except for her parents). She lives in San Francisco.

Kt Kilborn is an award-winning writer and performer in Atlanta, Georgia. A feminist trannie-boy, he wrote her honors thesis on performance art as social activism, and makes humorous, critical work from that aesthetic. Kt tours extensively, steering clear of public bathrooms. Find out more at www.ktkilborn.com.

Robbie Kirkland was 14-years-old when he committed suicide. His mother, Leslie Sadasivan, sent us these poems and shared his story. Robbie was teased and harassed in school from a young age because he was perceived as gay. He was not happy to be gay and felt rejected by his Catholic Church, our homophobic society, and his classmates. His family loved, supported, and accepted him but it was not enough. He would be 20 today if he were still alive. To learn more about Robbie's life, please go to the website *www.lgcsc.org/robkirkland/index.htm*.

Christa Kreimendahl, 20, lives in Florida. In the summer of 2000 she had two shorts *What a Tangled Web* and *IM SM* produced in Atlanta, Georgia by the Funny . . . That Way! Gay and Lesbian Repertory Theatre. Christa was given the "John Waters Writers Award" presented by Funny . . . That Way! and Deb Calabria. In the summer of 2001 her work *Radio Head* was produced by Stageworks in Tampa, and a staged reading of *Black-eyed Jack* was done by The Players Theatre in Sarasota.

Kristin is a MTF transsexual who will be attending a large Northeast public university in 2003, and majoring in psychology. She's not sure who she is, nor what will make her happy, but she knows they're both just around the next bend.

Mikhail Lewis has lived on both sides of Montana but doesn't know how to shoot a gun, ride a horse, or chew tobacco. In the past four months he's attended two universities and moved three times, all for love. Currently he's a music major at the University of Montana. This is his first time in print.

Tucker Lieberman graduated from Brown University with the class of 2002. He was the first-place winner of Transgender Tapestry's 2001 Poetry Contest and received Brown University's 2002 Casey Shearer Award for Excellence in Creative Nonfiction. *The Insatiable Adventures of the Eunuch Monks of Krat*, his first novel, is available from XLibris Press.

Meredith Matthews grew up south of Philadelphia in an upwardly mobile blue-collar set of neighborhoods as the kid named "Least Likely To Be Picked First For Kickball." A proudly politically-incorrect college dropout, she spends most of her time pushing papers in support of our nation's corrupt financial institutions, watching low-income housing applicants be systematically denied mortgages and home-improvement loans. With several prestigious state-level writing awards and publication credits from around the country under her belt, she slowly watches her child prodigy-colored aura fade and what little writing that's left start to be judged on the same abusive scale the rest of the world is held to. Thankfully, though, she's abandoned the world of poetry and taken the title "Eccentric Singer/Songwriter" in hopes of being held to a lower standard.

Theresa Elisabeth Molter is 22-years-old. Her first foray into writing was a story she wrote at age five entitled *The Littlest Butterfly*. She published her first 'zines when she was 14, and later studied creative writing, queer theory and child development at Hampshire. For her senior thesis, she wrote a full-length coming-of-age novel about queer teenagers, which she hopes to publish someday. Theresa currently lives in a small town on Shikoku Island in Japan with her girlfriend Gillian and a cat named Sweet Pea. She teaches English by day and by night is attempting to become involved in the Japanese queer scene. By the time you read this, however, she could be anywhere.

Wade Richards is the founder of StandOut!, a national gay and lesbian youth advocacy organization.

Davey S. is a won't-grow-up lostboy from Woodstock, New York. Ze works as an educator, activist, latex fairy, and all-around troublemaker in Northampton, MA, where ze lives with hir two roommates, two cats, and two red rat snakes. Hir favorite things are good pens, good drag, and juggling.

Shawnta Smith is a Jamaican/Belizean-Black American, 19-year-old lesbian from Brooklyn, New York. She has been an activist for the rights of Black young women and lesbians for five years and co-founded Sister Outsider, an organization in East Flatbush for young women who are self-supporting. Smith appeared in a 30-second commercial about young Black women and their perception of themselves, and became a public speaker at various national and regional youth conferences. She aspires to continue working in the non-profit field as a writer and artist while still impacting the lives of lesbian and young women of color.

Matthew Swanson is a 17-year-old queer youth who lives in La Crosse, Wisconsin. Matt is a junior at Central High School, and hopes to be accepted by the University of Wisconsin La Crosse after graduation. Matt is an active member of school committees, church, local community groups, and GALAXY—a gay and lesbian youth group in the area. In his spare time Matt can be found with his friends, out riding his bike, dancing his feet sore, or walking along enjoying a nice day. Matt's interests include art, theater, music, singing, computers, history, and education.

Wendy M. Thompson is a 21-year-old bisexual Chinese/African American poet, artist, feminist, and scholar from Oakland, California. She has been drawing and writing since she was five. Her literary work has appeared in anthologies such as *Restored Selves*, *Yell-Oh Girls*, and *Running for their Lives* as well as a variety of independent journals, 'zines, and online at generationrice.com. Her video, *stories from the blackasian planet*, aired in January 2003 on a public access program in Philadelphia and was screened at Ladyfest Lansing and Mujerfest in Texas in 2002.

Justin Tranter is a 21-year-old student from Chicago, who now lives in Boston. He's a singer, songwriter, and a poet. He's also the co-founder and president of Musicians with a Mission, a scholarship fund for the GLTB community. For more info check out www.justintranter.com.

tyger walsh is a 22-year-old/white/femme/activist/poet/massage therapist. She spent three years with Youth Speaks facilitating writing workshops for young women in juvenile hall and queer youth in San Francisco. She currently practices practice massage and herbal medicine and is dreaming of a free holistic health clinic.

Amy Weaver, a life-long author, began reading poetry at open-mikes in Dallas two years ago. In that time she has published two chapbooks and released a CD entitled *Naked*. She also was a member of the 2001 Championship Dallas SLAM team. Currently she is at work on a full-length book of poetry entitled *Naked Imagination*.

Grover Wehman is a trans-identified butch dyke leather boy drag king performance artist activist kid who resides in Brooklyn, New York. He is author of the 'zines *Permission to Speak Sir*, *Show Me Where it Hurts*, and *Why I'm inside the gates*. S/he is currently working on hir first novel and can be seen, heard, felt, and followed smashing the state in a town near you one orgasm, bike ride, and art piece at a time.

Anissa Weinraub, 23, remains the hair consultant to the queer/punk community of Providence, Rhode Island. As a creative writing mentor to high school students, she discusses empowered women's sexuality and the methods of countering the forces of hegemony. And she believes that the hottest place in hell is reserved for corporate real estate developers.

Han Yu is an artist. She studies at Harvard, and her website is www.hanacious.com.

[ABOUT THE EDITORS]

Diane Anderson-Minshall was co-founder and editor of *Girlfriends* magazine, *Alice* magazine, and *Roxie* magazine and she's currently the acting managing editor at *Curve* magazine. Her writing has appeared in dozens of publications including *Passport, Diva, Bitch, Bust, Venus, Film Threat, Utne Reader, Wine X, India Currents, Teenage, Seventeen, American Forests, Femme Fatale, The Advocate, Fabula, Natural Health, Pacific Sun,* and the *San Francisco Chronicle.* Her essays have also appeared in several anthologies including *Body Outlaws: Rewriting the Rules of Beauty and Body Image* (2004), *Closer to Home: Bisexuality and Feminism* (1992), *Young Wives Tales: New Adventures in Love and Partnership* (2001), and *Tough Girls* (2001). She edited and self-published the 1992 anthology *Lavender Locker: Writings by Gay, Lesbian, and Bisexual Youth.*

Gina de Vries, 21, is a white queer femme pervert who has been active in various queer, multi-issue, and sex activist circles since she came out in 1995. She was *Curve* magazine's "Hey! Baby" columnist for eight years, is a contributing writer for *On Our Backs* magazine, a founding member of the Come in Peace Collective, a board member for the Youth Gender Project, and an intern at the Center for Sex & Culture in San Francisco. She is still recovering from her stint as a queer youth poster child.

[RESOURCES]

NATIONAL

ORGANIZATIONS

Bisexual Resource Center
29 Stantiope St.
Boston, MA 02117
(617) 424-9595
www.biresource.org

COLAGE: Children of Lesbians and Gays Everywhere
3543 18th St. #17
San Francisco, CA 94110
(415) 861-KIDS
www.colage.org

Dignity USA (for LGBT Catholics)
1016 S. Wayne St. Apt. 611
Arlington VA 22204
Rfmiailo@aol.com

Family Diversity Projects
P.O. Box 1209
Amherst, MA 01004-1209
(413) 256-0502
www.lovesmakesafamily.org

Family Pride Coalition
P.O. Box 34337
San Diego, CA 92613
(619) 296-0199
www.familypride.org

Gay and Lesbian Victory Fund
1012 14th St. NW, Ste. 1000
Washington, D.C. 20005
(202) 842-8679
www.victoryfund.org

Gay, Lesbian, and Straight Education Network (GLSEN)
Through its network of 85 chapters in 35 states, works with school officials and parents to assure that each member of every school community is valued and respected, regardless of sexual orientation or gender identity.
121 West 27th St., Ste. 804
New York, NY 10001
(212) 727-0135
www.glsen.org

Gay-Straight Alliance Network (GSA Network)
A youth-led organization that connects school-based Gay-Straight Alliances (GSAs) to each other and to community resources. Through peer support, leadership development, and training, the GSA Network supports young people in starting, strengthening, and sustaining GSAs and builds the capacity of GSAs to: create safe environments in schools for students to support each other and learn about homophobia and other oppressions; educate the school community about homophobia, gender identity, and sexual orientation issues; and fight discrimination, harassment, and violence in schools.
Main office:
160 14th Street
San Francisco, CA 94103
(415) 552-4229
www.gsanetwork.org

Gay and Lesbian Medical Association (GLMA)
459 Fulton St., Ste. 107
San Francisco, CA 94102
(415) 255-4547
www.glma.org

Gay and Lesbian Alliance Against Defamation (GLAAD)
GLAAD promotes fair, accurate, and inclusive representation as a means of challenging discrimination based on sexual orientation or identity.
150 W. 26th St., #503
New York, NY 10001
(212) 807-1700 or (800) GAY-MEDIA
www.glaad.org

Gay & Lesbian National Hotline
Offers totally anonymous information, referrals and peer counseling. Callers can speak directly to a trained volunteer with access a national database of referrals specific to the gay and lesbian community.
(888) THE-GLNH
www.glnh.org

The Gender Identity Project
Offers transgender and transsexual people an opportunity to discover who they are in an atmosphere of self-acceptance and to build community.
(212) 620-7310
www.gaycenter.org/programs/mhss/gip.html

GenderPAC
332 Bleecker St., #K86
New York, NY 10014
(212) 645-2686
www.gpac.org

Hetrick-Martin Institute
An organization for NYC's GLBT youth that founded the Harvey Milk High School for queer youth.
2 Astor Place
New York, NY 10003
www.hmi.org
(212) 674-2400

Human Rights Campaign
919 18th St. NW, Ste. 800
Washington, D.C. 20006
(202) 628-4160
www.hrc.org

Institute for Gay and Lesbian Strategic Studies (IGLSS)
P.O. Box 2603
Amherst. MA 01004
(413) 577-0145
www.iglss.org

Lambda Legal Defense and Education Fund
120 Wall St., Ste. 1500
New York, NY 10005-3904
(212) 809-8585
www.lambdalegal.org

National Center for Lesbian Rights
870 Market St., Ste. 570
San Francisco, CA 94102
(415) 392-6257
www.nclrights.org

National Deaf Queer Resource Center
P.O. Box 14431
San Francisco, CA 94114
www.deafqueer.org

National Gay and Lesbian Task Force (NGLTF)
Sponsors the annual Creating Change conference for activists among other organizing.
1325 Massachusetts Ave. NW, Suite 600
Washington, DC 20005
(202) 393-5177
www.ngltf.org

The National Youth Advocacy Coalition (NYAC)
Maintains a database of local and national organizations that provide support services to lesbian, gay, bisexual, transgender, and questioning youth.
1-800-541-6922
www.nyacyouth.org

Parents, Families and Friends of Lesbians and Gays (PFLAG)
Offers a great support network for people coming out as well as for their families. Often there are PFLAG support group meetings in even small towns.
1726 M St. NW, Ste. 400
Washington, D.C. 20036
(202) 467-8180
(212) 463-0629
www.pflag.org

The Trevor Project
From the filmmakers behind Trevor *(a movie about a 13 year old boy's coming out), this organization aims to promote tolerance for gay and questioning youth, and to aid in suicide prevention among that group, by operating a national suicide prevention hot-line for gay youth.*
8950 West Olympic Blvd., Suite 197
Beverly Hills, California 90211
(800) 850-8087

STATE BY STATE

RESOURCES

There are far too many resources in many states to list here but we've included a few to get you started. Often one of the best places to find resources in your area, if you're near an urban or large suburban area, is the Lesbian, Gay, Bisexual, and Transgender Community Center. For a listing of community centers across the country, go to www.lgbtcenters.org.

ALABAMA

Gay and Lesbian Alliance of Alabama
4513 Highland Crest Circle
Birmingham, AL 35226
(205) 822-8830
gaydave@aol.com
ALASKA
Alaskans for Civil Rights
P.O. Box 214452
Anchorage, AK 99521-0072
(907) 274-9226
aem@alaska.net

Equality Under Alaskan Law
P.O. Box 244452
Anchorage, AK 99524
(907) 274-9226

ARIZONA

Arizona Human Rights Fund
P.O. Box 25044
Phoenix, AZ 85002-5044
(602) 650-0900
ahrf@aol.com

Valley of the Sun Gay and Lesbian Community Center
P.O. Box 33367
Phoenix, AZ 85067-3367
(602) 265-7283
www.phxcenter.org

ARKANSAS

Arkansas Equality Network
P.O. Box 25044
Fayettesville, AR 72702
(501) 222-6151
arequality@aol.com

CALIFORNIA

Diamond Street Youth Shelter
Shelter for homeless youth, 13-17
536 Central Ave.
San Francisco, CA 94040
415-567-1020

The Edge
39160 State St.
Fremont, CA 94538
(510) 790-2887
atfremont@aol.com

Gay and Lesbian Community Center
1006 E. Main St., Ste. 100
Ventura, CA 93001
(805) 653-1979

LYRIC (Lavender Youth Recreation & Information Center)
Support for LGBT youth, 23 and under.
(415) 863-3636
(800) 246-PRIDE

Pacific Pride Foundation
2225 S. Broadway #4
Santa Maria, CA 93454
(805) 963-3636
pride@silcom.com

San Francisco's LGBT Community Center
1800 Market St.
San Francisco, CA 94102
(415) 865-5555
www.sfcenter.org

San Francisco Women's Center
The Women's Building
3543 18th St.
San Francisco, CA 94110
(415) 431-1180

The Billy DeFrank Lesbian and Gay Community Center
938 The Alameda
San Jose, CA 95126
(408) 293-3040
www.defrank.org

Girlz Alliance
Girls Inc.
13666 E. 14th St.
San Leandro, CA 94577
(510) 357-5515

The Wayne McCaughan Community Pride Center
P.O. Box 3558
San Luis Obispo,CA 93403
(805) 541-4252

The Gay and Lesbian Community Services Center of Orange County
12832 Garden Grove Blvd., Ste. A
Garden Grove, CA 92843
(714) 534-0862
centeroc@millenia.com

L.A. Gay and Lesbian Center
1625 N. Schrader Blvd.
Los Angeles, CA 90028
(323) 993-7400
www.lagic.org

Rainbow Community Center of Contra Costa County
LGBT Youth Support Group, ages 13-21
2118 Willow Pass Road
Concord, CA 94518
(925) 692-0090
www.rainbowcc.org

Stonewall Alliance Center
P.O. Box 8855
Chico, CA 95927
(530) 893-3336
center@stonewallchico.org

Inland Empire Gay and Lesbian Center
P.O. Box 6333
San Bernardino, CA 92412
(909) 882-4488

The Lesbian and Gay Men's Community Center
P.O. Box 3357
San Diego, CA 92163
(619) 692-2077
www.thecentersd.org

Pacific Center for Human Growth
2712 Telegraph Ave.
Berkeley, CA 94705
www.pacificcenter.org

Spectrum Center for Gay, Lesbian and Bisexual Concerns
1000 Sir Francis Drake Blvd., Ste. 10
San Anselmo, CA 94960
(415) 457-1115
spectrumlg@aol.com

The Gay and Lesbian Community Center of Greater Long Beach
2017 E. 4th St.
Long Beach, CA 90814
(562) 434-4455
center@millenia.com

The Santa Cruz Lesbian, Gay, Bisexual and Transgendered
Community Center
P.O. Box 8280
Santa Cruz, CA 95061
(831) 425-5422
www.sclgbtcc.org

COLORADO

Equality Colorado
P.O. Box 300476
Denver, CO 80203
(303) 839-5540
www.equalitycolorado.org

Gay, Lesbian & Bisexual Community Services Center of Colorado
149 W. Oak St., Ste. 8
Fort Collins, CO 80524
(970) 221-3247

Pikes Peak Gay and Lesbian Community Center
P.O. Box 607
Colorado Springs, CO 80901
(719) 471-4429
www.ppglcc.org

CONNECTICUT

Hartford Gay and Lesbian Community Center
1841 Broad St.
Hartford, CT 06114
(860) 724-5542

New Haven Gay and Lesbian Community Center
P.O. Box 8914
New Haven, CT 06532
(203) 387-2252
nhglccinfo@aol.com

DELAWARE

ACLU Delaware, Lesbian and Gay Civil Rights Project
P.O. Box 700
Montachanin, DE 19710
(302) 654-3966
EqualityDE@aol.com

FLORIDA

Cosmopolitan Center of Miami
6445 NE 7th Ave
Miami, FL 33138
(305) 759-5210

The Family Tree
P.O. Box 38477
Tallahassee, FL 33307
(850) 222-8555
familytree1999@hotmail.com

The Gay & Lesbian Community Center
P.O. Box 71
Key West, FL 33041
(305) 292-3223
info@glcckeywest.org

Gay and Lesbian Community Center of Fort Lauderdale
P.O. Box 70518
Fort Lauderdale, FL 33307
(954) 563-9500
glccftl@aol.com

Triangle Gay, Lesbian & Bisexual Community Center of Central
Florida
P.O. Box 533446
Orlando, FL 32853
(407) 425-4527
www.glbcc.org

Triangle Community Center
1700 N. Dixie Hwy.
West Palm Beach, FL 33407
(561) 833-3638
compasswpb@aol.com

GEORGIA

Atlanta Gay and Lesbian Center
71 Twelfth St.
Atlanta, GA 30309
(404) 876-5372
www.aglc.org

Georgia Equality Project
P.O. Box 78351
Atlanta, GA 58357-2351
Execdir@gep.org

HAWAII

Gay and Lesbian Community Center
2424 S. Beretania St.
Honolulu, HI 96826
(808) 951-7000
glcc-news@juno.com

IDAHO

The Community Center
919 North 27th
Boise, ID 83703
(208) 336-3870
www.gayidaho.com/tcc

ILLINOIS

The Community Center
961 W. Montana St.
Chicago, IL 60614
(773) 472-6469

The Illinois Federation for Human Rights
(773) 244-3371
lfhr@suba.com

INDIANA

The Diversity Center
P.O. Box 441473
Indianapolis, IN 46806
(317) 639-4297
diversity@gayindy.org

Fort Wayne Education Community Center
3426 Broadway
Fort Wayne, IN 46807
(219) 744-1199

Justice, Inc.
915 W. 8th St.
Bloomington, IN 47404
(812) 334-8851

IOWA

Gay and Lesbian Resource Center
P.O. Box 7008
Des Moines, IA 50309
(515) 281-0634
outworld414@hotmail.com

Gay and Lesbian Resource Center of Cedar Rapids
P.O. Box 1643
Cedar Rapids, IA 52406
(319) 366-2055

Iowa Coalition for Human Rights
2320 York St.
Des Moines, IA 50316
(515) 262-9647
ichr@grizz.avalon.net

KANSAS

The Center—Wichita
P.O. Box 16746
Wichita, KS 67216
(316) 262-3991

Freedom Coalition of Kansas
913 Sunset Dr.
Lawrence, KS 66044
(785) 843-7256

KENTUCKY

Kentucky Fairness Alliance
P.O. Box 3912
Louisville, KY 40201
(502) 897-1973
mpricekfa@aol.com

LOUISIANA

Lesbian and Gay Community Center of New Orleans
2114 Decatur St.
New Orleans, LA 70116
(504) 945-1103

Lambda Baton Rouge
LGBT Community Center
2937 Greenwood Drive
Baton Rouge, LA 70808
(225) 383-0777
www.lambdabr.com

MAINE

The Diversity Center
RR 1, Box 1727
Limestone, ME 04750
(888) 216-2034 ext. 7299
pinkpride@hotmail.com

Gay and Lesbian Community Services Center of Northern Maine
P.O. Box 990
Cairbou, ME 04736
(207) 498-2088

MARYLAND

Gay and Lesbian Community Center of Baltimore
241 W. Chase St.
Baltimore, MD 21201
(410) 837-5445

MASSACHUSETTS

Boston Alliance for Gay Lesbian Bisexual Transgender
Questioning Youth (BAGLY)
14 Beacon St. #506
Boston, MA 02108
(617) 227-4313
www.bagly.org
Boston Center for Lesbians and Gay Men
80 Chandler St.
Boston, MA 02116
(617) 426-1316

Pride Zone
*A drop in center for GLBTQQA youth with support groups, peer
education program, drop-in, game nights, movie nights, and so on.*
2 Maple Ave #34
Northampton, MA 01060
(413) 584-1116
www.pridezone.org

MICHIGAN

Affirmations Lesbian and Gay Community Center
195 W. 9 Mile Rd., Ste. 106
Ferndale, MI 48220
(248) 398-7105
affirmationslgbt@juno.com

Kalamazoo Gay and Lesbian Resource Center
629 Pioneer St.
Kalamazoo, MI 49008
(616) 349-4234
kglrc@aol.com

Lesbian and Gay Community Network of Western Michigan, Inc.
909 Cherry St. SE
Grand Rapids, MI 49506
(616) 458-3511

The Triangle Foundation
19641 West Seven Mile
Detroit, Michigan 48219
877-787-4264

MINNESOTA

Aurora—A Northland Lesbian Center
32 E. 1st St.
Duluth, MN 55802
(218) 722-4903

District 202 Center for GLBT Youth
1601 Nicollet Ave
Minneapolis, MN 55403
(612) 871-5559
dist202@aol.com

Northland Gay Men's Center
8 N. 2nd Ave, Ste. 309
Duluth, MN 55802
(218) 722-8585

OutFront Minnesota
310 E. 38th Ste. 204
Minneapolis, MN 55409
(612) 822-0127
www.outfront.org

MISSISSIPPI

Mississippi Gulf Coast Community College Gay-Straight Alliance
2226 Switzer Road
Gulfport, MS 39507
DocLuvMBC@aol.com

MISSOURI

Gay and Lesbian Center of the Ozarks
P.O. Box 225
Springfield, MO 65801
(417) 869-3978
GLODir@aol.com

MONTANA

PRIDE!
P.O. Box 24106
Helena, MT 59624
(406) 442-9322
pride123@aol.com

Western Montana Gay and Lesbian Community Center
P.O. Box 7856
Missoula, MT 59802
(406) 543-2224
wmglcc@aol.com

NEBRASKA

Citizens for Equal Protection
P.O. Box 55548
Omaha, NE 68155-0548
(402) 398-3027
swinkler@unomaha.edu

Panhandle Gay and Lesbian Resource Support Services
P.O. Box 1046
Scottsbluff, NE 69363
(308) 635-8488

NEVADA

Gay and Lesbian Community Center of South Nevada
912 E. Sahara Ave
Las Vegas, NV 89104
(702) 733-9800

NEW HAMPSHIRE

Out and Equal
33 Rule St.
Keene, NH 3431
(603) 358-2167
bdenehy@top.monad.net

NEW JERSEY

Gay and Lesbian Youth in New Jersey
The Pride Center
1048 Livingston Ave.
North Brunswick, NJ 07710
www.galynj.org

Horizons Community Services, Inc.
P.O. Box 1316
Asbury Park, NJ 07712
(732) 774-1809

Rainbow Place of South Jersey
P.O. Box 2132
Voorhees, NJ 08043
(856) 848-2455

NEW MEXICO

Coalition for Equality in New Mexico
1451 Santa Cruz
Santa Cruz, NM 87505
(505) 983-5758

NEW YORK

The Audre Lorde Project (ALP)
A center for lesbian, gay, bisexual, two spirit, and transgender people of color.
85 South Oxford Street
Brooklyn, NY 11217-1607
(718) 596-0342
www.alp.org

Bisexual, Gay, Lesbian, and Transgender Youth of New
York (BiGLTYNY)
*Youth-run group for lesbian, transgender, bisexual, gay,
questioning or exploring, and queer-empowering young people ages
13 to 21.*
(212) 620-7310
www.gaycenter.org/orgs/bigltny/index.htm

Callen-Lorde Community HealthCenter
Health Outreach To Teens (HOTT) Program
Free, confidential, medical care and services to queers ages 13-21.
(212) 271-7200
www.callen-lorde.org

Gay Alliance of the Genesee Valley
179 Atlantic Avenue
Rochester NY, 14607
(716) 244-8640
www.gayalliance.org

Lesbian & Gay Community Services Center of New York
One Little West 12th St.
New York, NY 10014-2000
(212) 620-7310
www.gaycenter.org

New York University's Office of Lesbian, Gay, Bisexual, and
Transgender Student Services
New York University
New York, NY
(212) 998-4424
www.nyu.edu/lgbt

Pride Community Center of Central New York
P.O. Box 6608
Syracuse, NY 13217
(315) 426-1650

Queens Rainbow Community Center
PO Box 720464
Jackson Heights, NY 113720464
(718) 429-2300
www.queenspride.com

Safe Space and Safe Homes
For homeless, street involved and marginalized youths, offers food, housing, showers.
(212) 354-SAFE
www.kidsuccess.org

The Youth Enrichment Services (YES) Program
Lesbian and Gay Community Services Center
(212) 620-7310
www.gaycenter.org/programs/mhss/yes.html

NORTH CAROLINA

OutCharlotte, Inc.
P.O. Box 32062
Charlotte, NC 28232
(704) 563-2699
www.outcharlotte.org

Triangle Community Works
P.O. Box 5961
Raleigh, NC 27650
(919) 821-0055

NORTH DAKOTA

Equality North Dakota
P.O. Box 5222
Fargo, ND 58105-5222
(701) 235-7481
www.pridecollective.com

OHIO

Dayton Lesbian and Gay Center
P.O. Box 1203
Dayton, OH 45401
Daytonlgc@aol.com

Kaleidoscope Youth Center
P.O. Box 8104
Columbus, OH 43201
(614) 294-7886
www.kaleidoscope.org

Lesbian/Gay Community Service Center of Greater Cleveland
1418 W. 29th St.
Cleveland, OH 44113
(216) 522-1999
thecenter@earthlink.net

Stonewall Columbus Community Center
P.O. Box 10814
Columbus, OH 43201
(614) 299-7764
stnwall@ix.netcom.com

OKLAHOMA

The Center
2135 NW 39th St.
Oklahoma City, OK 73112
(405) 525-2437

OREGON

Flavors
For sexual minority youth of color, 24 and under.
503-417-7991

GLBTQ Youth Group
Amazon Community Center
2700 Hilyard St.
Willamette Valley, OR 97339
541-684-3466

LGBT Youth Group
Koinonia Center
14141 Kincaid St.
Eugene, OR 97401
541-346-1134

Gay, Lesbian, and Straight Education Network
Fighting anti-gay bias in K-12 schools.
12700 SW North Dakota St, #180
Tigard, OR 97223
503-525-1177

Lesbian Community Project
P.O. Box 5931
Portland, OR 97228
(503) 233-3913
lcppdx@hotmail.com

North Coast Pride Network
P.O. Box 1317
Astoria, OR 97103
(503) 338-0161
ncpn@pacifier.com

Phoenix Rising
424 E. Burnside St.
Portland, OR 97214
(503) 872-9664
safetnet@aol.com

Sexual Minority Youth Recreation Center (SMYRC)
Drop in and support programs for youth, including trans.
2100 SE Belmont St.
Portland, OR 97214
503-872-9664
TTY 503-231-9286
www.smyrc.org

PENNSLYVANIA

Gay and Lesbian Community of Pittsburgh
P.O. Box 5441
Pittsburgh, PA 19140
(412) 422-0114
glccpgh@aol.com

The Attic Youth Center
419 S. 15th Street (between Pine and Lombard)
Philadelphia, PA 19146
(215) 545.4331
www.atticyouthcenter.com

Mainline Youth Alliance
P.O. BOX 309
Wayne, PA 19087
(610) 688-1861
www.myaonline.org

William Way LGBT Community Center
1315 W. Spruce St.
Philadelphia, PA 19107
(215) 732-2220
wwcenter@yahoo.com

RHODE ISLAND

Rhode Island Alliance for Gay and Lesbian Rights
P.O. Box 5758
Weybossett Hill Station
Providence, RI 02903
(401) 521-4297
RIAlliance@aol.com

Rhode Island Gender Community (RIGC)
234 Lenox Ave.
Providence, RI 02907
www.rigc.org

Youth Pride, Inc.
134 George M. Cohan Blvd.
Providence, RI 02903
(401) 421-5626
youth_pride@yahoo.com

SOUTH CAROLINA

South Carolina Pride Center
1108 Woodrow Street
Columbia, SC 29205
(803)771-7713
www.scglpm.org

SOUTH DAKOTA

The Center
613 South Main Avenue
Sioux Falls, SD 57104
(605) 331-1153
www.discoverthecenter.com

TENNESSE

The Center for Gay, Lesbian, Bi & Transgender Life in Nashville
703 Barry Road
Nashville, TN 37204
(615) 297-0008

Memphis Gay and Lesbian Center
P.O. Box 41074
Memphis, TN 38174
(901) 324-4297

TEXAS

Austin Latino/a Lesbian and Gay Organization
1715 East 6th St., Ste. 112
Austin, TX 78702
(512) 472-2001
allgoinc@aol.com

Houston Lesbian and Gay Community Center
P.O. Box 2304
Houston, TX 77252
(713) 524-3818
hlgcc@neosoft.com

John Thomas Gay and Lesbian Community Center
P.O. Box 190869
Dallas, TX 75219
Dallasglcc@resourcecenterdallas.org
UTAH
The Lesbian and Gay Community Center of Utah
361 N. 300 W.
Salt Lake City, UT 84103
(801) 539-8800

VERMONT

Outreach, Inc.
P.O. Box 5883
Burlington, VT 05402
(802) 860-1044
VIRGINIA
Shenandoah Valley Gay and Lesbian Association
PO Box 1023
Harrisonburg, VA 22801
540-574-4636
www.svgla.org

WASHINGTON

Lesbian Resource Center
2214 S. Jackson St.
Seattle, WA 98144
(206) 322-3965

The Rainbow Community Center
206 ½ Wellesley
Spokane, WA 99207
(509) 458-2741 box 5
www.4pride.net/r2c2

Rainbow Center
1501 Pacific Ave, Ste. 310D
Tacoma WA 98402
(253) 383-2318

WEST VIRGINIA

West Virginia Lesbian and Gay Coalition
P.O. Box 11033
Charleston, WV 25339
(304) 343-7305
wvglc@aol.com

WISCONSIN

The Gay Youth Wisconsin Hotline
Gay Youth Milwaukee
P.O. Box 090441
Milwaukee, WI 53209
1-888-GAY-TEEN
414-272-8336 (in the Milwaukee area)

Outreach
Madison's LGBT Center
600 Williamson Street
Madison, WI 53703-3588
608.255.8582
www.outreachinc.com

WASHINGTON, D.C.

Sexual Minority Youth Assistance League
410 7th Street, SE
Washington, DC 20003-2707
(202) 546-5940
www.smyal.org

WYOMING

Teen Human Rights Network
P.O. Box 7424
Jackson Hole, WY 83002
(800) GAY-TEEN

United Gays and Lesbians of Wyoming
P.O. Box 6837
Cheyenne, WY 82003
www.uglw.org

University of Wyoming LGBTA
Laramie, WY 82070
(307) 745-4232
www.uwyo.edu/lgbta

Wyoming Youth Pride Project
P.O. Box 1676
Laramie, WY 82070

INTERNATIONAL ORGANIZATIONS

International Gay and Lesbian Human Rights Commission
(IGLHRC)
1360 Mission St., Ste. 200
San Francisco, CA 94103
(415) 255-8680
www.iglhrc.org

International Gay and Lesbian Association
81 Kolenmarkt,
B 1000, Brussels, Belgium
+32-2-5022471
www.ilga.org

Outfront
Amnesty International's Program on Human Rights and Sexual
Identity
322 8th Ave
New York, NY 10001
(212) 633-4200
www.amnesty-usa/group/outfront

World Pride
Circolo Mario Meili
Via Corinto, 5
00146 Roma Italia
www.WorldPride2000.com

[BOOKS]

There are dozens of books out now for lesbian, gay, trans, bisexual, intersex, and other so-called "sexual minority" youth. We can't possibly list all of them here. Books are available through women's bookstores, gay bookstores, indies (like Powells.com), chains like Barnes & Noble, and the ubiquitous Amazon.com. In fact, as the publish-on-demand world expands, a number of young queer authors are self-publishing—making their books harder to get at indy bookstores. Our advice? Shop around for what you want at Amazon.com and then go to either your local bookstore or to your library and ask them to order it. Here are a few books to get your started.

P.S. Yes, we know, we could have done it in bibliography format but we hated that part of high school as much as the rest of you. So here's our listing, arranged by book title.

100 QUESTIONS AND ANSWERS ABOUT AIDS: What You Need to Know; Ford, Thomas Michael. This book also contains interviews with young people who know first hand how AIDS affects people's lives.

ACT WELL YOUR PART; Sakers, Don; This novel follows high schooler Keith, who dislikes his new school, Oak Grove High. He misses his old friends, and wonders if he'll ever fit in. Then, he joins the school's drama club, where he meets the boyish Brian Davenport.

ALF; Vogel, Bruno; The story of a friendship between two boys at a Berlin prep school, Felix and Alf. Fearful of the sexual side of their relationship, Alf enlists in the German army, and his letters from the front radicalize his friend, who becomes an agitator against the war.

ALL-AMERICAN BOYS; Mosca, Frank; "I've known I was gay since I was thirteen . . . . It was the most natural thing in the world. I thought everyone was. At least until I hit high school the next year. That's when I finally realized all those faggot and dyke jokes referred to people like me." Say no more.

ALWAYS MY CHILD; Jennings, Kevin; A parents guide to understanding their young gay, lesbian, bisexual, transgendered, or questioning son or daughter. It also includes a chapter in which real teens describe how they feel towards their own parents during this time in their lives.

AM I BLUE? COMING OUT FROM THE SILENCE; Bauer, Marion Dane; Sixteen prominent young adult authors offer original short stories that explore aspects of growing up lesbian or gay or with lesbian or gay parents.

ANNIE ON MY MIND; Garden, Nancy; A baby dyke classic— chosen by the American Library Association as one of the Best of the Best Books for Young Adults in the seventies— follows a young woman who is just coming to terms with her lesbianism.

AUBADE; Martin, Kenneth; When it was first published in 1957, this novel created a storm of controversy with its frank revelations about adolescent homosexual feelings. This re-release, with a new intro by the author, is written in the first person by a sixteen-year-old Irish boy.

BECOMING VISIBLE: A Reader in Gay & Lesbian History for High School & College Students; Jennings, Kevin, editor; An anthology of works that every library should carry, edited by a gay high school teacher. Demand to read it in history class.

BLACKBIRD; Duplechan, Larry; A gay black high school boy survives an exorcism.

BODIES THAT MATTER: On the Discursive Limits of Sex; Butler, Judith; A challenging approach to "sex" as a social construct from a great feminist theoretician.

BODY ALCHEMY: Transsexual Portraits; Cameron, Loren; Combines self-portraits and portraits of other transsexual men with personal essays about his gender transition.

BOYS LIKE HER: Taste This; Camillerri, Anna, Coyote, Ivan E., Eakle, Zoe, and Montgomery, Lyndell; Originally a stage show, this collection of performances by the Taste This collective includes poems, stories, and short essays about gender, sexuality, and family.

BOYS ON THE ROCK; Fox, John; The story of Billy Connors, high school student, swim team member and all-around regular guy who has to face the fact that he's gay.

BRIDGES OF RESPECT: Creating Support for Lesbian and Gay Youth; American Friends Service Committee; This guide is presented as an invitation to adults who work with youth to recognize the needs of a neglected, largely invisible population of lesbian and gay young people. It includes an extensive listing of resources—print and audiovisual materials as well as organizations, programs, and projects—useful to educators, health care and social service providers, and youth advocates.

THE CAT CAME BACK; Mullins, Hilary; A girl at boarding school in early eighties has affairs with a teacher and a coach and eventually develops a crush on a female fellow student.

CHANGELINGS; Sinclair, Jo; Two teenage girls, one Jewish and one black, forge a friendship as their neighborhood seethes with racial strife. This novel shows how such struggles affect younger generations, whose survival lies in their power to love.

CODY; Hale, Keith; A teen coming out classic, now back in print. This novel explores a different type of friendship where the lines between straight and gay blur, where two minds merge, making each one whole in the process.

COLONIZE THIS! Young Women of Color on Today's Feminism; Hernandez, Daisy and Bushra Rehman (editors); Anthology of essays on feminism among women of color.

COLOUR OF HIS HAIR; Rees, David; Two teens fall in love in the mid-seventies. When their so-called friends at school find out what is going on, the persecution begins. The relationship survives into early adulthood, and ten years later, it undergoes some surprising twists and turns in less liberal, AIDS-conscious 1986.

CRUDDY; Barry, Lynda; It's 1971, five years after the Lucky Chief Motel Massacre, after which Roberta, now 16, was found wandering the desert, covered with blood. Even now, she still won't talk about what happened. She lives with her mother and sister, hides in the weeds during her lunch period, and befriends some misfits like herself.

CRUSH; Futcher, Jane; The *Sweet Valley High* of queer teen novels, written in the eighties.

CRYSTAL BOYS; Hsien-yung, Pai; The first Chinese novel with a gay theme, was later made into the film *Outcasts*. Cast out from his family after coming out, A-qing, the adolescent hero, drifts into a life of hustling among the buoliquan, or "glass community" (Taiwanese for the gay community in which individuals are called "crystal boys").

DARE, TRUTH OR PROMISE; Broock, Paula; Two girls fall in love while working at a burger joint and deal with the ensuing aftermath when everyone finds out.

DEATH BY DENIAL: Studies of Suicide in Gay and Lesbian Teenagers; Remafedi, M. A 1989 federal study found that teenagers struggling with issues of sexual orientation were three times more likely than their peers to commit suicide. The report was swept aside by the Bush administration, yet the problem didn't go away. Here are the full findings of that report, and of several other studies documenting the difficulties faced by teenagers who are coming out, proposing ways to ease the process.

DROWNING OF STEPHAN JONES; Greene, Bette; When a gay couple moves to the artsy community near town, Carla is not the least bit offended. However, Andy, the boy she adores, wages war against the men. A tragic night of violence leads Carla to realize that Andy's heinous actions can no longer be denied, and she must stand up for what she believes in.

EDINBURGH; Chee, Alexander; Haunting and beautiful novel in which a Korean-American boy deals with a serial pedophile and a young gay love amidst a boys choir setting.

ENCHANTED YOUTH; McMullen, Richie; It's 1958 and fifteen-year-old Richie discovers the excitement of Soho in the rock and roll era and the love for a public school guy his own age.

FREE YOUR MIND: The Book for Gay, Lesbian, and Bisexual Youth and Their Allies; Bass, Ellen; A nineties-era basic primer on youth issues.

GAY AND LESBIAN YOUTH; Herdt, Gilbert; The changes in youth in the United States is compared and contrasted with those changes elsewhere to better understand the identities, situation, and relationships of queer teens in many societies.

GENDER OUTLAW; Bornstein, Kate; One of the first books about trans people to be written by an actual trans person. Bornstein couples autobiography with theory in this account of her trans life.

GENDER SHOCK: Exploding the Myths of Male and Female; Burke, Phyllis; A frightening account of how gender identity disorder in children is used to identify kids engaging in "gender inappropriate" behaviors and "treat" them through psychiatric evaluation and incarceration.

GENDER TROUBLE; Butler, Judith; A landmark book of gender theory and queer theory. Must read, even for non-academics.

GIRL WALKING BACKWARDS; Williams, Bett; One of the more recent and realistic portrayals of queer teens includes a lesbian narrator who is already, more or less, "out."

GOOD MOON RISING; Garden, Nancy; Sweetly dated story in which two girls work together on a school play and find their feelings stretch beyond friendship. Their schoolmate sets out to discredit them as sinners.

THE GOOD TIMES ARE KILLING ME; Barry, Lynda; A pre-teen Edna forms an unlikely friendship with tough girl Bonna. Because Edna is white and Bonna is black, there are pressures from both sides against their friendship. At the same time, we are witness to the tensions in Edna's family and in her neighborhood, which is going through the early stages of integration, all told through a series of short vignettes in Edna's very distinctive voice.

GROWING UP GAY: A Literary Anthology; Singer, Bennett, editor; A collection of over fifty coming of age stories pairs selections by lesbian and gay teenagers with older writers' reflections on growing up gay or lesbian. Selections written by James Baldwin, Rita Mae Brown, Quentin Crisp, and Martina Navratilova among others.

HAPPY ENDINGS ARE ALL ALIKE; Scoppetone, Sandra; Two girls, young love, the last summer before college.

THE HARVEY MILK INSTITUTE GUIDE TO LESBIAN, GAY, BISEXUAL, TRANSGENDER AND QUEER INTERNET RESEARCH; Ellis, Alan, Highleyman, Liz, Schaub, Kevin, and White, Melissa, editors; Reference toolkit for researchers who need to access queer resources on the Internet.

IN YOUR FACE: Stories from the Lives of Queer Youth; Gray, Mary L.; A collection of queer teen stories from academic publisher Haworth.

IS IT A CHOICE? Answers to 300 of the Most Frequently Asked Questions about Gay and Lesbian People; Marcus, Eric. The title says it all.

THE JOURNEY OUT: A Guide for and About Lesbian, Gay, and Bisexual Teens; Pollack, Rachel. Another basic primer.

LARK IN THE MORNING; Garden, Nancy; Gillian's diary is stolen and in it she confesses her love for Suzanne, who shares the same feelings. When Gill tracks down the thieves, they are a couple of young runaways escaping their abusive parents. Respecting their fear she decides to help them but soon discovers she may have taken on too much.

THE LAST TIME I WORE A DRESS; Scholinski, Daphne; Scholinski's memoir of the four years she spent in a mental institution as a teenager after being diagnosed with Gender Identity Disorder in Children (GIDC).

LIKE THE LION'S TOOTH; Kellogg, Marjorie; At a school for troubled kids, eleven-year-old Ben and his outcast friends learn to cope with the effects of their parents' savagery.

LOOKING QUEER; Atkins, Dawn; Research, poetry, theory, and essays that address the special needs of queer and trans people who are dealing with eating disorders and body image issues.

MANIFESTA: Young Women, Feminism, and the Future; Baumgardner, Jennifer and Richards, Amy; A mix of history, politics, and pop culture that looks at young women in the post-nineties world.

MOVIE HOOKY; Foster, Dan; William Carfax discovers movies; especially, those that glamorize violence and extreme suffering. As often as possible he plays hooky to go the movie palaces of Dallas. There he replaces his humdrum life with the loves and hates of beautiful men and women. Very slowly, he comes to understand and accept his homosexuality and leaves Texas for New York and its glittering promises.

MY CHILD IS GAY: How Parents React When they Hear the News; McDougall, Bryce, editor. A classic paperback on the many reactions you can expect.

MY GENDER WORKBOOK; Bornstein, Kate; a workbook that challenges society's ingrained ideas about how women, men, and those in between should act.

OUTING YOURSELF: How to Come Out as Lesbian or Gay To Your Family, Friends, or Coworkers; Signorile, Michelangelo. It's not specific to younger people but it's a great primer for some basics that will help anyone ease of the closet.

THE PHALLUS PALACE: Female to Male Transsexuals; Kotula, Dean (editor). Essays and photographs about FTMs that spans the range of issues from gender identity, physical transformation, medical issues, and historical highlights.

PINK THINK: Becoming a Woman in Many Uneasy Lessons; Peril, Lynn. Dissects the assumptions about behavior expected of women.

THE PERKS OF BEING A WALLFLOWER; Chbosky, Stephen; A 14-year-old, lonely teenage boy encounters everyday struggles including crushes, drug experimentation, depression, and a queer best friend.

PRAYERS FOR BOBBY: A Mother's Coming to Terms with the Suicide of her Gay Son; Aarons, Leroy. If your Christian parents are having a hard time coming to terms with your sexuality, get them this book.

QUEER KIDS: The Challenges and Promise For Lesbian, Gay, and Bisexual Youth; Owens, Robert E. Another academic tome that parents and teachers might enjoy.

RAINBOW BOYS; Sanchez, Alex. If you're a gay guy just coming out, this book might look a bit more like your life then memoirs from the eighties.

THE SECRET DIARY OF ADRIAN MOLE, AGED 13 ¾; Townsend, Sue; The hilarious "journal" of a British teenage boy named Adrian Mole.

SEX CHANGES: The Politics of Transgenderism; Califia, Patrick; A book of theory, politics, and history around trans identity and the trans movement.

THE SHARED HEART: Portraits and Stories Celebrating Lesbian, Gay, and Bisexual Young People; Mastoon, Adam; Lovely photos by Mastoon accompany text by about 30 young queers writing about themselves and their lives.

SOME OF THE PARTS; Cooper, T; A novel about a gay man, his genderfreak friend, and the family that surrounds them.

STIR-FRY; Donoghue, Emma; Maria has just moved to Dublin to attend the university, and moves into an apartment with two slightly older women who turn out to be a couple. Through them, Marie realizes her own sexuality and struggles to choose between the two when they break up and both reveal their desire for her.

STONE BUTCH BLUES; Feinberg, Leslie; A seminal novel about butch/femme lesbian and trans life as well as labor activism in the fifties.

STRAIGHT PARENTS, GAY CHILDREN: Inspiring Families to Live Honestly and with Greater Understanding; Bernstein, Robert A. Another one where the title says it all.

TALES OF THE CITY (series); Maupin, Armistead; A series of novels about the interconnected lives of the residents of an apartment house in San Francisco, including many queer characters and one trans character.

TRANSGENDER WARRIORS: Making History from Joan of Arc to Dennis Rodman; Feinberg, Leslie; A book of trans and genderqueer history, including a chapter of interviews and photographs with trans people today.

TRANS LIBERATION: Beyond Pink or Blue; Feinberg, Leslie; A collection of Feinberg's essays and speeches around trans and genderqueer issues.

TRYING HARD TO HEAR YOU; Scopettone, Sandra; The 16 year old Camilla recounts a crucial summer in which her close knit theater group discovers that two of their members are gay.

TWO TEENAGERS IN TWENTY: Writings by Lesbian and Gay Youth; Heron, Ann; A sequel to one of the earliest gay teen books, *One Teenager in Ten*. In it a new generation of teens describe first-hand what it's like to be gay or lesbian in a world that wants to condemn them. Many of the essays here are combined with some from the first book.

UNDERSTANDING SEXUAL IDENTITY: A Book for Gay and Lesbian Teens; Rench, Janice; This book offers support for gay and lesbian teens and answers questions that many people have about sexual identity. A simple, compassionate, and factual starting point for gay teens and people who care about them. Offers a straightforward, no-nonsense approach to understanding sexuality.

WE'RE NOT ALONE; Isensee, Rik; A heartfelt tale depicting the breakdown of barriers between a young man and woman who happen to be gay, their heterosexual friends, their school teachers, and their parents. This story empowers gay and lesbian youth to overcome homophobia and develop a positive identity.

WEETZIE BAT; Block, Francesca Lia; A young girl and her gay best friend try to find life and love in the wilds of Los Angeles.

WHAT HAPPENED TO MR. FORSTER?; Bargar, Gary W.; Louis is trying to make his sixth-grade year a success, and is being helped by a new teacher, Jack Forster. But parents are suspicious of the bachelor teacher, and he disappears suddenly. Why?

WHEN HEROES DIE; Durant, Penny Raife; 12-year-old Gary Boyden idolizes his uncle Rob, a former basketball star who is outgoing and took the place of Gary's father when he ran off. But Rob's been sick lately, and Gary's mother reveals that Rob is not only gay, but has AIDS. Soon Gary is forced into doubts about his own sexuality, his relationship with his uncle, and what really constitutes a hero in people's eyes.

WHEN SOMEONE YOU KNOW IS GAY; Cohen, Susan and Daniel; Written for straight teenagers on the subject of homosexuality, this book combines interviews and personal accounts with historical and scientific material.

THE WORLD OF NORMAL BOYS; Soehnlein, K.M.. Another great coming of age book.

THE XY SURVIVAL GUIDE; Nycum, Benjie; A guide to coming out, avoiding drama, starting a gay-straight alliance, and dealing with discrimination from the gay youth magazine *XY*.

THE YEAR OF ICE; Malloy, Brian; A beautiful coming out story about a 17-year-old jock.

THE YEAR THEY BURNED THE BOOKS; Garden, Nancy; A rare and lively book about teens coming out that doesn't focus on first love. Two high school newspaper players find love and battle the administration in a sort of free speech meets meets queer love.

* *A portion of this list was culled from Lambda Rising bookstore's gay youth best-sellers list.*

[OTHER RESOURCES]

FILMS, VIDEOS, DVDS

By now you probably know all about the great queer kid flicks that have come out in the last decade. But where to get them? Many libraries and schools will now order them. Check out the lesbian-owned Wolfe Video (www.wolfevideo.com) for the most comprehensive collection of queer films on VHS and DVD. Some suggested first films to check out: *Edge of Seventeen, Get Real, All Over Me, Incredibly True Adventures of Two Girls in Love, But I'm a Cheerleader, Different for Girls, Beautiful Thing, Ma Vie En Rose, Boys Don't Cry, A Boy Named Sue, The Brandon Teena Story, Gendernauts, XXXY,* and *By Hook or By Crook.*

QUEER MEDIA

There are now several dozen magazines, newspapers, and newsletters for LGBT readers. You can find the latest listing in *The Harris Guide* (Upstart Press) which is author Paul Harris's very extensive directory of LGBT print and broadcast media.

LGBT newspapers are often distributed free at gay bookstores, coffeehouses, and community centers. Cities as far and wide as Boise, Idaho (*Diversity*) and Charlotte, North Carolina *(Q Notes)* each have queer newspapers. If you can't find one, try trolling the Internet for a local listing. As far as magazines, here are some key national publications:

The Advocate: A weekly national LGBT newsmagazine (think *Time* with queers). 323-871-1225 or www.advocate.com.

Anything that Moves: A quarterly journal for bisexuals. 415-626-5069 or www.anythingthatmoves.com.

Curve: The best-selling lesbian magazine in the country. 415-863-6538 or www.curvemag.com.

FTM Newsletter: A quarterly newsletter for female to male transgender and transsexual people. 415-553-5987 or www.ftm-intl.org.

Gay Black Female: A California-based monthly magazine. 323-376-2157 or www.gayblackfemale.com.

Girlfriends: Another national lesbian magazine. 415-648-9464 or www.girlfriendsmag.com.

OUT: A national gay and lesbian magazine with lots of fashion. 323-871-1225 or www.out.com.

Trikone: A quarterly for queer Southeast Asians. 415-789-7322 or *www.trikone.org.*

White Crane Journal: A quarterly journal of gay men's spirituality. P.O. Box 2762, Wimberley, TX 78676-2762. www.whitecranejournal.com.

XY: A young gay men's monthly. 415-552-4666 or www.XY.com.

'ZINES

Most 'zines are put out by independent publishers who often charge between one to two dollars for an issue (and sometimes as little as the cost of postage). Write to these folks or check out their websites for details on their 'zines and how to order them.

DUST RISING by Zachary Strassburger (*ostraussey@yahoo.com*): A personal and political 'zine about trans and intersex issues.

LION + LAMB by Riley Demland (*lionpluslamb@hotmail.com*): A personal 'zine about trans issues and identity.

PERMISSION TO SPEAK, SIR by Grover Wehman (*groverboi@yahoo.com*): A political 'zine about trans, bds/m, and youth issues.

PUSSYBOY by Johnny Schilling *(pussboy@angelfire.com):* A personal and political 'zine about trans and youth issues from a punk and anarchist perspective.

TIM TUM by Micah *(micahrebelprince@hotmail.com):* A personal and political 'zine about trans and Jewish identities.

TRANSFEMINISM: A COLLECTION by Emi Koyama (www.eminism.org): A collection of Koyama's writings on trans, feminist, and transfeminist issues, as well as multi-issue organizing.

CONFERENCES

Creating Change, an annual conference of activists by the National Gay & Lesbian Task Force.www.ngltf.com/cc.

Genderblast!, for TGIQ youth, 25 and under, and their adult allies. Sponsored by the Youth Gender Project. www.youthgenderproject.org.

National Youth Advocacy Coalition hosts a national queer youth (25 and under) conference in Washington, D.C. every year, as well as regional conferences. www.nyacyouth.org.

Southern Comfort is an all-inclusive gender conference in Atlanta, Georgia. www.sccatl.org.

Teaching Respect for All is the **Gay, Lesbian, Straight Education Network's** annual conference for youth and educators. *www.glsen.org.*

Transcending Boundaries is a Northeast regional conference on transgender, bisexual, intersex, and other sexual minority community issues. www.transcendingboundaries.org.

True Spirit is a conference on various permutations of FTM and transmale identity. Everyone is welcome. It is usually held in Washington, D.C. in February. www.true-spirit.org.

Young, Loud, and Proud, a conference sponsored by San Francisco's Lavender Youth Recreation & Information Center, is for queer youth 25 and under, as well as their adult allies. www.lyric.org.

WEBSITES

Do remember that some queer websites might be blocked by software that is meant to filter out pornography.

Ambient Joven: The Spanish language resource for queer youth.*www.ambientjoven.org.*

Bitch Magazine: A gay-positive, feminist response to pop culture. *www.bitchmagazine.com.*

Broder 13: This is Braden Jahr's personal website about the struggles of growing up gay. *www.broder13.com.*

Bust Magazine: Probably the coolest glossy girl mag on the planet. www.bust.com.

Emi Koyama: Emi is self-described as "a multi-issue social justice slut synthesizing feminist, Asian, survivor, dyke, queer, sex worker, slut, intersex, genderqueer, and crip politics," as these factors, while not a complete descriptor of who she is, all impacted her life. Emi is currently the Program Assistant for Intersex Society of North America and runs two kick ass personal sites: www.eminism.org and *www.transfeminism.org.*

Feminist Campus: An excellent resource for young feminists that includes listings of campus pro-choice groups and statewide alliances as well as articles on leadership, reproductive rights, and even Hollywood feminists. *www.feministcampus.org.*

Gay.Com: Up to the minute news with portals for several different cultural communities as well as other countries (particularly Latin America). *www.gay.com.*

GenderPAC: The Gender Public Advocacy Coalition's page for news and resources. They also run the annual National Conference on Gender. *www.gpac.org.*

Indie Gurl: A great guide to cool grrrl sites on the web. *www.indiegurl.com.*

Intersex Society of North America: Full of information and resources, including suggestions on how *you* can help intersex activists. *www.isna.org.*

LesbiaNation: The online community for lesbians that offers lots of news, entertainment, travel, health, and other articles and resources. *www.lesbianation.com*

Live Journal: LiveJournal.com is a free service that allows anyone to create and customize an online journal. It's already host to several communities about gender issues including androgyny, female2me, ftmstudents, genderoutlaws, genderqueer, intersexed, mtf, partners_of_tg, soffa, transgender, transguysgroup, transminds, transpartners, transpauper, transteachers, transvestism. To find any community, enter www.livejournal.com/users/insert name of community here/).

Metropolitan Community Church: A great resource for Christian kids who might be unwelcome at their own churches. MCC is a worldwide fellowship of Christian churches that offer special outreach to lesbian, gay, bisexual, trans, and other queer folks. The site has a listing of churches all over the U.S. www.ufmcc.com.

My Sistahs: A health resource site for young women of color, with particular emphasis on HIV and STDs. *www.mysistahs.org.*

National Youth Advocacy Coalition: aimed at improving the lives of LGBTQ youth, their URL is *www.nyacyouth.org.*

Oasis Magazine: The first and largest writing community for queer youth. www.oasismag.com.

Out Proud: Nice site by the National Coalition for Gay, Lesbian, Bisexual & Transgender Youth. *www.outproud.org.*

Planet Out: A comprehensive news and entertainment website with a teen page that includes a listing of top 50 colleges for queer kids, a coming out survival guide, lists of queer teen movies, and queer youth message boards. It also operates Jenni Olson's kick-ass queer movie compendium, PopcornQ. www.planetout.com.

Poz Youth: A great website, a project of Advocates for Youth, that is aimed at HIV-positive (poz) youth and their peer advocates. www.youthHIV.org.

Scarlet Teen: The premier website for teens to get information about sex. *www.scarleteen.com/gaydar.*

Strap On: The progressive, queer-centered, sex-positive, girl-friendly online community.

Fabulous message boards and forums for discussion, including a trans forum. *www.strap-on.org.*

TechnoDyke: The super-sassy, female-focused, and web savvy gathering place for lesbian, bisexual, and trans dykes. www.technodyke.com.

TGTS-Youth: An email discussion list for young people under 26 who are transgendered, transsexual, gender-bending, or questioning their gender. www.geocities.com/transboys/tgts-youth.html

Too Tall Blondes: This is a website for sex activist/educator Barbara Carrellas and her partner performance artist/author Kate's Bornstein. It's chock-a-block with fun stuff from Bornstein, author of *Gender Outlaw, My Gender Workbook,* and *Nearly Roadkill.* www.tootallblondes.com

Transgender Warrior: The personal website of author and activist Leslie Feinberg, who penned the brilliant novel *Stone Butch Blues* as well as *Trans Liberation: Beyond Pink and Blue.* www.transgenderwarrior.org.

Youth Guardian Services: A youth-run, non-profit organization that provides support services on the Internet to gay, lesbian, bisexual, transgendered, questioning, and straight supportive youth. *www.youth-guard.org.*

Youth Resource: A great national resource for young people, with particular focus on queer youth. Offers one of few online resources for deaf youth, as well. *www.youthresource.com/feat/deaf.*

[GLOSSARY]

There are a million different ways that people identify themselves these days. We couldn't possibly agree on all the definitions but here is a short list to start with. This glossary was culled partially from the Youth Gender Project (with the help of our contributors) and doesn't necessarily reflect the editors' or publishers' opinions.

Ableism: Discrimination against disabled people, which results from the system of oppression that gives power and privilege to temporarily-able-bodied people at the expense of disabled people.

Ageism: Discrimination against youth and/or seniors; results from the system of oppression that gives power and privilege to those perceived as adults, at the expense of those perceived as (or who actually are) "young" or "old."

Ally: A member of any dominant group in society who works to dismantle any form of oppression from which they benefit.

Androgynous: Someone who reflects an appearance that is both masculine and feminine or who appears to be neither (or both) a boy and a girl

Anti-racist: A term generally applied to white people, refers to an individual who makes a conscious choice to *act* to challenge the white supremacy system, including their own white privilege.

Bigendered: Refers to those who feel they have both a male and a female side to their personalities. Some "bigendered"

people cross-dress, others may eventually have a sex-change operation, others may do neither.

Birth Sex/Sex: The sex one is assigned at birth due to the perception of existing external sex organs. Once this determination is made, it becomes a label used for raising the child in either one gender image or other (either as male or female).

Bisexual: Anyone who has an attraction to males and females, regardless of whether they engage in sex with both.

Boi: A biological woman or trans guy with a boyish presentation or identification.

Classism: Discrimination against working class or poor people that results from capitalism.

Cross Living: Living full-time in the preferred gender image, opposite to one's assigned sex at birth, sometimes in preparation for a sex change operation. Some transpeople live full time in their preferred gender image, in stealth passing, but never intend to have a sex change operation.

Direction: Which way one is crossing the gender line. Masculine/Male to Feminine/Female (MTF) is one way, Feminine/Female to Masculine/Male (FTM) is another.

Drab: Means "Dressed as a Boy," referring to men's clothes or in men's clothes; used mainly by gender benders and cross-dressers of both directions.

Drag: Originally used in Shakespeare's Globe Theater to mean "Dressed As Girl," referring to male actors (there were no actresses) playing female roles. Now mainly used by gender benders and cross-dressers of both directions. Many radical communities believe drag is the performance of masculine or feminine identity, regardless of clothing, or as the "art of consciously performing gender."

Drag Queen/ Drag King: Used to refer to gender benders or cross-dressers of both directions who wear women's clothes (drag queens) or men's clothes (drag kings), often in a flamboyant or exaggerated way

FTM: Female-to-male (transvestite or transsexual).

Gay: People who are attracted to, in love with, or have sexual relations with members of the same sex. Most commonly used to refer to men who self-identify as homosexual.

Genderqueer: Can mean a person who deviates from gender norms, consciously or unconsciously. The term genderqueer is commonly claimed as an identity by many youths to explain their gender identity and expression as one that is not set, binary, or one that conforms to any gender standard (whether it be a assigned at birth gender or a gender norm within FTM or MTF communities)

Gender Dysphoria: Literally, it's being unhappy with the gender you are physically anatomically, prior to any changes. Full-blown "gender dysphoria syndrome" is the same as transsexualism.

Gender/Gender Identity: The hard-to-define sense of "being male" or "being female" that is usually in accord with, but sometimes varies from, physical anatomy. There is no clear agreement on how gender identity is formed, but most current theories say that gender identity is formed before birth. Gender is the culture assigned to one at birth as being male or female and enforces notions of characteristics given to males and females. Gender identity then is the identification of ones internal gender feelings within or outside of the binary gender system regardless of assigned gender culture. Many lesbian-feminists believe that there is no such thing as a physical anatomical gender—arguing that gender can be masculine/feminine but not male/female. Many people, though, use the word interchangeably with sex.

Gender Binary System: A system of oppression that requires everyone to be raised either male or female, and masculine or feminine. Eliminates the possibility for other gender expressions, and gives power to people whose genders do not break gender norms at the expense of transgender and intersex people. The system also places one gender in a more privileged position and inherently the other gender at the bottom.

Gender Expression/ Gender Image: The way one presents themselves to the world, as either masculine or feminine, or both or neither

Genetic: Refers to the chromosomal endowment of the individual, with emphasis on the sex chromosomes (XX in women and XY in men).

Heteroflexible: A straight person with an affinity for queer culture. An ally.

Heterosexism: A system of oppression that gives power to straight people at the expense of queers, by saying that heterosexuality is the only form of healthy sexual expression. Manifests itself in the institutions that seemingly promote heterosexuality by recognizing those relationships.

Hir/Ze: Gender neutral pronouns created and used within the trans community. Often adopted by those who identify as genderqueer as their pronoun preference. Used in place of he and him, she and her. Also, a polite usage of pronouns when a person's desired pronoun preference is not known and cannot be asked. Pronounced "hear" and "see."

Intersex: Born with partial sex organs of both genders or ambiguous genitalia. About 1 in 2000 infants born are at risk for intersex genital mutilation. An even higher proportion of the population is intersex in some way. This word replaces "hermaphrodite," which is generally considered impolite and/ or derogatory.

Lesbian: Most commonly used to refer to women who are attracted to, in love with, or have sex with members of the same sex. Is also used as a term of definition by feminists (or womyn) who politically identify with other women and abstain from sexual relations with men.

Male supremacy: A system of oppression that gives power to men and values masculinity, at the expense of women and femininity.

MTF: Male to Female (transvestite or transsexual).

No-Ho: Means "non-hormonal" and describes someone who does not choose to make their gender transition through the hormonal process. This could be for social, personal, political, medical, or financial reasons.

Non-Op: Transsexuals who seek sex reassignment through hormones and who cross-live, but stop just short of surgery. Some have concerns about major surgery, which is not always successful, others are unable to pay for the expensive procedures surgery would entail, and still others feel that they are complete without the surgery.

Oppression: Results from the *use* of institutional power and privilege where one person or group *benefits at the expense* of another. Oppression is the use of power and the effects of domination.

Pansexual: A person who is attracted to many genders across the spectrum.

Pass: To be in your preferred gender image and to be able to do so convincingly in the eyes of those around you. (E.g. an FTM, cross dresser, or drag king whose look is accepted as representing a man's and not a woman's.)

Post-Op: A transsexual who has had their sex change operation and now has the physical anatomy which mimics that of the sex they have transitioned to.

(Institutional) Power: Is control, access and influence. In our society power means having *control* of and *access* to ruling institutions; freedom from the threat of being questioned or reprimanded for wrong-doing; and the ability to define standards and norms.

Present: Refers to gender expression and the process of reflecting ones gender to others; someone who is bigendered may present as female one day and male the next

Pre-Op: A transsexual who has not yet had their sex change operation(s) but who plans on having it/them.

Privilege: Is a right, a favor, immunity, or an advantage specially granted to one individual or group and *withheld* from another.

Queer: A term co-opted by activists in the late eighties, refers to people who primarily identify as a sexual minority of some sort such as gays, lesbians, intersex individuals, etc. Can also be used to mean "odd" or "different" and so has been embraced by a variety of (mostly younger) sex activists.

Racism: Discrimination against people of color that results from the white supremacy system of domination, and can cross racial and cultural groups. Racism is prejudice plus institutional power.

Self-Identify: Refers to the process of people choosing with which identifying terms/groups they identify. (Eg. Someone could self-identify as male, female or bigendered, multi-racial, etc.)

Sexism: Discrimination against women that results from the male supremacy system of oppression.

Sex-Reassignment Surgery (SRS): Commonly used in place of the offensive phrase "sex change operation." It is used instead because many people feel that they were always the sex/gender they are. "Sex change" puts the focus on the body makeup as opposed to the individual identity, whereas sex reassignment surgery is physically aligning the body or genitals to match the sex one identifies as.

Socialized: Referring to the "training" process that takes place once birth sex is determined/decided upon. People whose birth sex is female are "socialized" as women although they may or may not self-identify as women

Systems of oppression: Interlocking societal, economic, moral, and religious values that keep many groups of people down to ensure the power and advantage of a few groups or one group of people. Some systems of oppression in the U.S. and Europe include: heterosexism, male supremacy, white supremacy, the gender binary system, and capitalism.

TGIQ: An acronym for trans, genderqueer, intersex, and questioning.

Trannydyke: A transgender person attracted to people with a feminine gender.

Trannyfag: A transgender person attracted to people with a masculine gender.

Trans: An abbreviation of transgender.

Trans Female/Woman: An MTF. The medical literature tends to use the extremely demeaning term "male transsexual" to mean the same thing. Note that you can tell the preferred form is in use when the gender word comes after the "T" word.

Transfeminism: The ways in which transgender and intersex individuals synthesize their feminist experiences.

Transgender (TG): Refers to a group of all people who are inclined to cross the gender lines, including transsexuals, cross-dressers, bigender people, gender benders, and any others who identify as gender variant. This is the main way the word is used today, and is referred to as the "umbrella definition" as it covers everyone.

Trans Liberation: A phrase that, according to trans author Leslie Feinberg, has come to refer to the empowerment of all those who blur or bridge the boundary of the sex or gender expression they were assigned at birth: cross-dressers, transsexuals, intersex people, Two Spirits, bearded females, masculine females and feminine males, drag kings and drag queens.

Trans Man/Male: An FTM. The medical literature tends to use the extremely demeaning term "female transsexual" to mean the same thing. Note that you can tell the preferred form is in use when the gender word comes after the "T" word.

Transphobia: Discrimination, fear or hatred of people who blur traditional gender lines that results from the gender binary system. Often comes from one's own insecurity about being a "real man" or a "real woman."

Transsexual (TS): Anyone who identifies as the "opposite" sex than the one they were born into, including anyone who wants to have or has had a sex-change operation. Not all transsexuals choose hormones or surgery.

Transition: The change from assigned gender norms to desired gender identity. This could include name and/or pronoun change, change in clothing, body or community in order to be comfortable as the gender they identify as. This may include fully transitioning ones life and body to live as a male or a female, or may include transitioning in a small community, such as family, subset of friends, or in the larger world.

Transvestite/Cross Dresser (CD): Someone who, from time to time, wears clothes opposite of their birth sex, to relieve gender discomfort or a feeling of gender dysphoria. Transvestite is a word from the medical establishment, and is not often used by transgender people themselves.

White supremacy: A system of oppression that gives power and advantages to white people at the expense of all other people.

Ze/Hir: [See hir above.]

[CREDITS &

ACKNOWLEDGMENTS]

Alicia Champion's lyrics are © 1999 NightChild Music, ASCAP

Alicia Brook's essay, "Talking Dirty" originally appeared in the 'zine *Slut*.

Our glossary has been adapted with permission from an earlier publication of Youth Gender Project.

Wade Richards monologue originally appeared as part of an interview by Jeff Walsh, editor of *Oasis Magazine* (oasismag.com). It is reprinted here with their permission.

Printed in the United States
118401LV00003B/42/A